SO...YOU COME HERE
OFTEN?

 I'm glad you picked me up today, and am looking forward to this journey of gratitude with you.

First Printing, 2017

ISBN 978-0-692-94536-0

WANT ALEXSYS TO SPEAK ABOUT TRYBAL GRATITUDE AT YOUR NEXT EVENT?
Visit www.alexsysthompson.com

Design and formatting by The Offbeat Writer.
www.theoffbeatwriter.com

THIS JOURNAL BELONGS TO

A WONDERFULLY GRATEFUL SOUL

IF FOUND, PLEASE CONTACT ME AT:

(BE SURE TO USE THE SECRET CODEWORD:)

POTENTIAL BENEFITS OF RETURNING THIS:

(AND A CRISP HIGH-FIVE, WHICH NEVER GOES OUT OF STYLE)

THANK YOU

FOR JOINNG OUR TRYB OF GRATITUDE

THIS TRYB IS ALL ABOUT

LIVING A LIFE OF **GRATITUDE**,

SELF-CARE, CONNECTION, & ABUNDANCE

OUT LOUD.

THE WORLD NEEDS MORE OF THESE THINGS, &

YOU ARE THE ANSWER.

DEDI**CATION**

TO ALL THE AWE-INSPIRING WOMEN WHO'VE COME INTO MY PATH.

Through my gratitude journey, I've been able to connect with amazing people who inspire me every day. I am so grateful and humbled by the lovely experiences that have unfolded on my journey because of these extraordinary women. With you, the ordinary becomes the spectacular.

Gratefully,

SPECIAL **THANKS**

TO THE PEOPLE WHO MADE THIS JOURNAL POSSIBLE.

To Liv Hadden and Darlena Eggebrecht for making this journal come to life. To Kay Taylor, Suzi Pomerantz, and Barry Spilchuk for the honor of sharing your words of support in this journal.

"Can we be grateful for the *tough* stuff?"

FORE**WORD**

We have all had **"stuff"** happen to us in our lives. Good stuff and bad stuff is inevitable as we navigate our way through this thing called **life.**

It's easy to be grateful for our families, friends and the many blessings we have all been granted – it's *easy* – but sometimes we forget.

Can we be grateful for the tough stuff?

What do you do when "the yogurt hits the fan?"

As someone who has survived two serious cancer-scares, an accident, an employee stealing our money and assorted other maladies – I can say with certainty – **gratitude** is the secret fuel that allowed me to bounce back from each and every setback.

My belief system and my ability and willingness to be grateful – no matter what the circumstances – have always put me back on track.

I love how this book teaches us to be **grateful** *and* **graceful** – or, as I sometimes like to spell them – **great-full** *and* **grace-full**. Each of these two traits demonstrates our ability to be gentle and powerful at the same time.

Allow this book to be your daily companion and you will soon experience the *magic of gratitude*.

Many blessings to you,

Barry Spilchuk
Coauthor, *A Cup of Chicken Soup for the Soul*
Founder, www.TheLEGACY.club

HEY GOOD LOOKIN'

WHY TRYBAL GRATITUDE?

Trybal is a community of choice defined by the understanding and acceptance of "try"ing. Before each wonderful success, there are often many "trys". The gratitude Tryb we are creating with each person along this journey is one of safety, celebration, and humility.

WELCOME

TO YOUR **GRATITUDE JOURNEY**

I AM EXCITED YOU ARE HERE.

This book is a culmination of a lifetime of practice, failure, and more practice. It feels great to be able to share some concepts and rituals I have developed to live my authentic life.

Should you choose to take this journey of introspection through the window of a gratitude practice, you will inevitably unveil your authentic self.

I HAVE HAD A CONSISTENT

(NOT PERFECT)

PRACTICE OF

GRATITUDE

JOURNALING

FOR OVER A

DECADE.

IMPERFECTION **WELCOME**

The first couple of years, my practice started and stopped. I was seeking perfection, which meant even one missed day was a failure. One day, I decided to throw in the towel; what was the point if I couldn't be perfect?

Eventually, I realized there was no need to beat myself up. I collected my journal from the corner I'd tossed it into, dusted it off, and started again.

As soon as I stopped making myself wrong for missing a day (or three) and started to celebrate the days I was leaning into my gratitude practice, everything changed.

I, _____,
COMMIT TO BEING
GRACEFUL
WITH MYSELF ON MY
GRATITUDE **JOURNEY.**

BE GRACEFUL WITH YOURSELF · CELEBRATE THE DAYS YOU STEP INTO GRATITUDE · THE RECIPE FOR SUCCESS IS DYNAMIC, SPICY, SMOOTH, AND BOLD · WHEN OUR FILTERS CHANGE SO DO OUR EXPERIENCES ·

So, be graceful with yourself, keep at it. Somewhere along the way, it will become a longing, and the simple act of misplacing your journal will create some anxiety. In that moment, you can sit back and smile— **you have a gratitude practice**.

THE RECIPE FOR SUCCESS IS

NOT **NEW**, *NOT* **HARD**, *NOT* **SPECIAL**.

IT IS **DYNAMIC**

SPICY, SMOOTH &

BOLD.

THIS JOURNEY IS **YOURS**

The recipe for success is yours; you have all the ingredients within the life you live.

When we make a practice of slowing down long enough (5-10 minutes a couple of times a day) to take an inventory of what we want out of each day and the gifts that each day has offered, our filters change. Much like a camera, when our filter changes, so does the way we experience life.

I have used over a dozen wonderful journals in my practice and have integrated some of the features I loved most about them here. I've also added some key features I found myself missing or making room for.

The design is meant to be very fluid or circular like the process itself. You will find spaces to write, doodle, create lists, etc. The color scheme is muted purposefully—*you* add color and life to these pages. So, feel free to color outside the lines!

LET ME EXPLAIN MY INTENTIONS WITH THE LAYOUT, **AND THEN YOU CAN MAKE IT YOURS!**

On the following pages, you'll find one of my daily entries, which you can use as a roadmap.

(I believe feedback is a gift: as you start to use the journal, please feel free to drop me a note at www.alexsysthompson.com to let me know what you loved and any features you would like to see in future editions.)

I was smart enough to go through any door that opened.

JOAN RIVERS

DATE **5** / **6** / 20**17**   ○ ○ ○ ○ ○ ○ ●
                                  S M T W TH F S

GETTING STARTED

I am grateful for:

Coffee on the patio and time to write in my journal

The opportunity to present solutions to a new client

Maggy (my dog's) "love you no matter what" attitude

Today's intention (in a word):   **ACCEPTING**

Supporting behavior(s):

I will remain curious when learning what my potential client, team mates, and family really need. When I feel myself jumping in with a solution, I will gently remind myself I am here to learn not solve in the moment. If I catch myself offering solutions, I will pull back and return to being curious.

WRAPPING UP

So, how did your day go?   ☹ 😐 🙂 😊

What's your high-five to yourself?

Magical Moments:
(moments/people/experiences)

Intention you'd like to take into sleep with you?

SPACE TO **EXPLORE**

YOU WILL HAVE A QUOTE TO START EACH DAY.

I have enjoyed this feature as it helps me ponder life through the lense of the quote.

The date and day allows some flexibility for the days you don't make it to your journal—**no guilt!**

WRITE 1-3 THINGS YOU ARE GRATEFUL FOR.

Do this as early as you can in your day. I love the days I do this before my feet hit the floor or when I have time to enjoy curling up on the patio with my journal and a cup of coffee.

SET YOUR INTENTION FOR THE DAY.

I choose my word of the day in a couple of ways: by pulling something from the "I am grateful for" section (under "Getting Started") forward, or by taking a few minutes to meditate on what I would like to experience as the day unfolds.

Once you choose your word, it helps to write it on a post-it note in your car, on your monitor, or wherever you will see it several times that day.

JOT DOWN SUPPORTING BEHAVIORS.

This brings the gratitude and intention into awareness through actions. This part of my journaling started to shift my reality as my actions and intentions became much more congruent.

This drives the idea that **thoughts turn into actions** and allowed me to understand how to manifest abundance for myself and those around me.

I was smart enough to go through any door that opened.

JOAN RIVERS

DATE _5_ / _6_ / 20_17_

○ ○ ○ ○ ○ ○ ◉
S M T W TH F S

GETTING STARTED

Curious!

WHY?

I am grateful for:

Coffee on the patio and time to write in my journal

The opportunity to present solutions to a new client

Maggy (my dog's) "love you no matter what" attitude

MARGIN
MADNESS

Today's intention (in a word): **ACCEPTING**

How?

So what?

Supporting behavior(s):

I will remain curious when learning what my potential client, team mates, and family really need. When I feel myself jumping in with a solution, I will gently remind myself I am here to learn not solve in the moment. If I catch myself offering solutions, I will pull back and return to being curious.

INNOVATE · DOODLE · THINK · REMEMBER · POPPED UP · MUSINGS

⑥

TIRED
=
WINE

FRUSTRATION
=
CARBS

WRAPPING UP

So, how did your day go? ☹ 😐 😀 😊

What's your high-five to yourself?

I was able to remain curious when with potential client. I shared I would be able to outline a few paths forward for discussion. They received it well and are going to the next round!

Magical Moments:
(moments/people/experiences)

Intention you'd like to take into sleep with you?

SPACE TO **EXPLORE**

USE THE FREE SPACE ANY WAY YOU LIKE.

Margin madness is often the area where some of my best ideas start to move into reality. It is a place to use however you want. Don't think too hard; let the feelings you are experiencing show up in the margins, let your dreams loose...it's a space to just let go. **Have fun!**

TAKE INVENTORY OF HOW YOU FEEL.

The end of your day is a great time to check-in with yourself and see how you're doing—nothing complicated, just choose an emoticon that feels right. In the empty space surrounded by words, elaborate about any of the day's downloads, feelings, events, thoughts, etc.

CELEBRATE THE GOOD STUFF.

Over the years, I've learned the value of celebrating along the way. That's why there is a space for your high-five moment of the day. It's a place to allow yourself some self-love by celebrating the simple things you did well or are proud of.

I remember writing that I was proud of an entire month of consistently bringing all the shopping carts back into the store so no one's car was damaged.

It doesn't have to be Earth-shattering. Start small. Remember, these pages are yours. Let go and stretch into this.

I was smart enough to go through any door that opened.

JOAN RIVERS

DATE **5** / **6** / 20**17**

S M T W TH F ●S

GETTING STARTED

I am grateful for:

Coffee on the patio and time to write in my journal

The opportunity to present solutions to a new client

Maggy (my dog's) "love you no matter what" attitude

Today's intention (in a word):   ACCEPTING

Supporting behavior(s):

I will remain curious when learning what my potential client, team mates, and family really need. When I feel myself jumping in with a solution, I will gently remind myself I am here to learn not solve in the moment. If I catch myself offering solutions, I will pull back and return to being curious.

WRAPPING UP

So, how did your day go? 😞 😐 😊 🙂

What's your high-five to yourself?

> I was able to remain curious when with potential client. I shared I would be able to outline a few paths forward for discussion. They received it well and are going to the next round!

Magical Moments:
(moments/people/experiences)

> When I came home tired and ready for a glass of wine, Maggy greeted me with a wiggly butt and a desire to cuddle. The need for wine was replaced with some furry friend love.

Intention you'd like to take into sleep with you?

> The desire to continue to be aware of what food/drink I am craving when I am tired, frustrated, etc. Turning this awareness into positive action so I can live the healthy life I want to live.

SPACE TO **EXPLORE**

RECOGNIZE THE MAGIC.

Magical moments are those times when something or someone got your attention in a way that felt good and added value to your day.

Hint: the magic is often within a human connection or a moment of vulnerability. Allow them to blossom.

SET YOURSELF UP FOR SUCCESS.

As you wrap up your nightly routine, jot down a problem you are wrestling with, something you can't seem to find a solution for—really anything that is driving your mental monkey bananas.

The simple act of writing it down will allow your guides to assist you while you sleep. I cannot count the number of "problems" I have solved in my sleep with this simple practice. It also aids in helping me rest as I hand over the matters of the mind.

THE MAGIC OF GRATITUDE

IS SO MULTI-FACETED.

MY WISH IS FOR YOU TO

EXPERIENCE

IT ALL!

Gratitude in Action

Food-sharing is an innate way that we show our love for people we care about. Including others in times of celebration is an act of kindness.

DR. THERESA NICASSIO

Share a meal with someone you've been meaning to reconnect with.

ACTION TAKEN:	FEELINGS EXPERIENCED:
Called Jill (who I had not seen in person for 18 months) we are both in town—scheduled dinner for next week!!!	Had a very good time and it was like we never missed a beat. We lost time and scheduled a dinner for twice a year in places we both want to visit. Regret I didn't do this earlier.
THINGS LEARNED/ OBSERVED:	WOULD I DO THIS AGAIN? WHY?
Thinking about someone isn't the same as letting them know or spending time with them. Planning is required to make it come to life.	YES! I have reached out to 2 other friends that I haven't seen in a long time and we are working on getting something scheduled. Hope to not fall into this slump again.

TURN IT INTO **ACTION**

This journal was created to help you move gratitude into action for yourself and others.

Every now and then, you'll come upon a "Gratitude in Action" page designed to help you move gratitude into the world in a way that promotes kindness, love, and connectedness.

You'll actually have the opportunity to execute the exact example you see here!

DESIGNED TO MANIFEST GRATITUDE.

There is a quote to set the mood, and then a request for you to move gratitude into the world with someone else.

While not every action may speak to you, I do hope you will act on the ones that do, with the goal of at least one a month.

Once you have taken action, make time to catalog the experience in the space provided.

The process of slowing down to document your feelings and experiences will bring another level of awareness to you. That awareness will open new doors and windows you had not seen before. These doors and windows are to be explored and add zest to your life.

ENJOY THE JOURNEY!

Don't take life so seriously, and live with as few regrets as possible.

"We take for granted the very things that *most* deserve our gratitude."

-Cynthia Ozick

IGNITE YOUR
GRATITUDE

SECOND CHANCES

A SUPPORT SYSTEM

NATURE

WAKING UP EVERY MORNING

GOOD HEALTH

THE RAIN

GAINING PERSPECTIVE

COMMUNITY

KIND **WORDS**

SMILING

LAUGHTER

FRIENDS **& FAMILY**

THE SUN

BOOKS & MUSIC

CLEAN WATER

THE LITTLE THINGS

SPIRITUAL **CONNECTION**

FEELING HOPE

INNER PEACE

FINDING LOVE

GOOD, HAPPY MEMORIES

COFFEE

LEARNING

*May your eyes be open to let the wonders of the world
and, in response, your heart and soul awaken.*

ALEXSYS THOMPSON

DATE __1__ / __24__ / 20__18__   ○ ○ ○ ● ● ○ ○
                                       S M T W TH F S

GETTING STARTED

I am grateful for:
faith
friends
family
house & everything in it
garage & my car

life
health talents
gifts &
God gave me

Today's intention (in a word):   content

Supporting behavior(s):
focus on little things
be in one moment
enjoy the moment

WRAPPING UP

So, how did your day go?   ☺

What's your high-five to yourself?

> over 6000 steps

Magical Moments:
(moments/people/experiences)

> listening to kids read
> singing in the choir

Intention you'd like to take into sleep with you?

> contentment

A man has free choice to the extent that he is rational.

THOMAS AQUINAS

DATE ____ / ____ / 20____

○ ○ ○ ○ ○ ○ ○
S M T W TH F S

GETTING STARTED

I am grateful for:

Today's intention (in a word):

MARGIN
MADNESS

Supporting behavior(s):

WRAPPING UP

So, how did your day go? ☹ 😐 🙂 😊

What's your high-five to yourself?

Magical Moments:
(moments/people/experiences)

Intention you'd like to take into sleep with you?

MUSINGS · POPPED UP · REMEMBER · THINK · DOODLE · INNOVATE

When a woman tells the truth she is creating the possibility for more truth around her.

ADRIENNE RICH

DATE ____ / ____ / 20____

○ ○ ○ ○ ○ ○ ○
S M T W TH F S

GETTING STARTED

I am grateful for:

Today's intention (in a word):

Supporting behavior(s):

WRAPPING UP

So, how did your day go? ☹ 😐 🙂 😊

What's your high-five to yourself?

Magical Moments:
(moments/people/experiences)

Intention you'd like to take into sleep with you?

Anyone who has a why to live can bear almost any what.

NIETZSCHE

DATE ____ / ____ / 20____

○ ○ ○ ○ ○ ○ ○
S M T W TH F S

GETTING STARTED

I am grateful for:

Today's intention (in a word):

Supporting behavior(s):

MARGIN
MADNESS

WRAPPING UP

So, how did your day go? ☹ 😐 🙂 😊

What's your high-five to yourself?

Magical Moments:
(moments/people/experiences)

Intention you'd like to take into sleep with you?

MUSINGS · POPPED UP · REMEMBER · THINK · DOODLE · INNOVATE

*And suddenly you know: it's time to start something new
and trust the magic of new beginnings.*

MEISTER ECKHART

DATE ____ / ____ / 20____   O O O O O O O
                                   S M T W TH F S

GETTING STARTED

I am grateful for:

MARGIN
MADNESS

Today's intention (in a word):

Supporting behavior(s):

MUSINGS · POPPED UP · REMEMBER · THINK · DOODLE · INNOVATE

WRAPPING UP

So, how did your day go? ☹ 😐 🙂 😊

What's your high-five to yourself?

Magical Moments:
(moments/people/experiences)

Intention you'd like to take into sleep with you?

*As we express our gratitude, we must never forget that the
highest appreciation is not to utter words but to live by them.*

JOHN F. KENNEDY

DATE _____ / _____ / 20_____

○ ○ ○ ○ ○ ○ ○
S M T W TH F S

GETTING STARTED

I am grateful for:

Today's intention (in a word):

MARGIN
MADNESS

Supporting behavior(s):

WRAPPING UP

So, how did your day go? ☹ ☺ ☺ ☺

What's your high-five to yourself?

Magical Moments:
(moments/people/experiences)

Intention you'd like to take into sleep with you?

MUSINGS · POPPED UP · REMEMBER · THINK · DOODLE · INNOVATE

Start where you are. Use what you have. Do what you can.

ARTHUR ASHE

DATE ____ / ____ / 20____

○ ○ ○ ○ ○ ○ ○
S M T W TH F S

GETTING STARTED

I am grateful for:

MARGIN
MADNESS

Today's intention (in a word):

Supporting behavior(s):

WRAPPING UP

So, how did your day go? ☹ 😐 😊 😀

What's your high-five to yourself?

Magical Moments:
(moments/people/experiences)

Intention you'd like to take into sleep with you?

MUSINGS · POPPED UP · REMEMBER · THINK · DOODLE · INNOVATE

Gratitude in Action

You don't know about real loss because it only occurs when you've loved something more than you love yourself.

ROBIN WILLIAMS

Create a list of three or more people you love, then tell them.

ACTION TAKEN:	FEELINGS EXPERIENCED:
THINGS LEARNED/ OBSERVED:	**WOULD I DO THIS AGAIN? WHY?**

Sometimes, carrying on, just carrying on, is the super human achievement.

ALBERT CAMUS

DATE _____ / _____ / 20_____

○ ○ ○ ○ ○ ○ ○
S M T W TH F S

GETTING STARTED

I am grateful for:

MARGIN
MADNESS

Today's intention (in a word):

Supporting behavior(s):

WRAPPING UP

So, how did your day go? ☹ 😐 🙂 😊

What's your high-five to yourself?

Magical Moments:
(moments/people/experiences)

Intention you'd like to take into sleep with you?

MUSINGS · POPPED UP · REMEMBER · THINK · DOODLE · INNOVATE

Always remember that you are absolutely unique. Just like everyone else.

MARGARET MEAD

DATE ____ / ____ / 20____   O O O O O O O
                                   S M T W TH F S

GETTING STARTED

I am grateful for:

Today's intention (in a word):

MARGIN MADNESS

Supporting behavior(s):

WRAPPING UP

So, how did your day go? ☹ 😐 ☺ 😊

What's your high-five to yourself?

Magical Moments:
(moments/people/experiences)

Intention you'd like to take into sleep with you?

MUSINGS · POPPED UP · REMEMBER · THINK · DOODLE · INNOVATE

Put your ear down close to your soul and listen.
ANNE SEXTON

DATE ____ / ____ / 20___

○ ○ ○ ○ ○ ○ ○
S M T W TH F S

GETTING STARTED

I am grateful for:

MARGIN
MADNESS

Today's intention (in a word):

Supporting behavior(s):

WRAPPING UP

So, how did your day go? ☹ 😐 🙂 😊
What's your high-five to yourself?

Magical Moments:
(moments/people/experiences)

Intention you'd like to take into sleep with you?

INNOVATE · DOODLE · THINK · REMEMBER · POPPED UP · MUSINGS

SURPRISE!

I'll be popping in from time to time to cheer you on, share a story, or just say hello.

When I first heard about this gratitude practice thing, I fully believed I could muscle into it through sheer determination. The way to a full life is paved with hard work and sacrifice, right? A commitment of any kind can feel tough at the beginning—I've found finding grace can ease the feeling of "hard" in some pretty spectacular ways. I say this after having received many blessings from a decade of practicing gratitude.

So, consider this a high-five from me to you for being here and creating the life you want to live, one day at a time.

I will share some personal stories along the way to inspire you to keep on keepin' on.

Create a great day—I will see you again on another page.

My mission in life is not merely to survive, but to thrive:
and to do so with some passion, some compassion, some
humor, and some style.

MAYA ANGELOU

DATE ____ / ____ / 20____

○ ○ ○ ○ ○ ○ ○
S M T W TH F S

GETTING STARTED

I am grateful for:

MARGIN
MADNESS

Today's intention (in a word):

Supporting behavior(s):

INNOVATE · DOODLE · THINK · REMEMBER · POPPED UP · MUSINGS

WRAPPING UP

So, how did your day go? ☹ 😐 😊 🙂

What's your high-five to yourself?

Magical Moments:
(moments/people/experiences)

Intention you'd like to take into sleep with you?

I must admit that I personally measure success in terms of the contributions an individual makes to her or his fellow human beings.

MARGARET MEAD

DATE _____ / _____ / 20_____

○ ○ ○ ○ ○ ○ ○
S M T W TH F S

GETTING STARTED

I am grateful for:

Today's intention (in a word):

MARGIN MADNESS

Supporting behavior(s):

WRAPPING UP

So, how did your day go? ☹ 😐 🙂 😊

What's your high-five to yourself?

Magical Moments:
(moments/people/experiences)

Intention you'd like to take into sleep with you?

MUSINGS · POPPED UP · REMEMBER · THINK · DOODLE · INNOVATE

Gratitude in Action

Be curious, not judgmental.
WALT WHITMAN

Spend one day taking inventory of your internal conversations that judge things, people, situations, etc. Just create the awareness.

ACTION TAKEN:	FEELINGS EXPERIENCED:
THINGS LEARNED/ OBSERVED:	**WOULD I DO THIS AGAIN? WHY?**

We shall not cease from exploration, and the end of all of our exploring will be to arrive where we started and know the place for the first time.

T.S. ELIOT

DATE _____ / _____ / 20_____

○ ○ ○ ○ ○ ○ ○
S M T W TH F S

GETTING STARTED

I am grateful for:

Today's intention (in a word):

MARGIN
MADNESS

Supporting behavior(s):

WRAPPING UP

So, how did your day go? ☹ 😐 😃 ☺

What's your high-five to yourself?

Magical Moments:
(moments/people/experiences)

Intention you'd like to take into sleep with you?

MUSINGS · POPPED UP · REMEMBER · THINK · DOODLE · INNOVATE

Do not go where the path may lead, go instead where there is no path and leave a trail.

RALPH WALDO EMERSON

DATE ___ / ___ / 20___

○ ○ ○ ○ ○ ○ ○
S M T W TH F S

GETTING STARTED

I am grateful for:

Today's intention (in a word):

Supporting behavior(s):

WRAPPING UP

So, how did your day go? ☹ 😐 😊 ☺

What's your high-five to yourself?

Magical Moments:
(moments/people/experiences)

Intention you'd like to take into sleep with you?

Gratitude is the fairest blossom which springs from the soul.
HENRY WARD BEECHER

DATE ____ / ____ / 20____   ○ ○ ○ ○ ○ ○ ○
S M T W TH F S

GETTING STARTED

I am grateful for:

Today's intention (in a word):

MARGIN
MADNESS

Supporting behavior(s):

WRAPPING UP

So, how did your day go? ☹ 😐 🙂 😊
What's your high-five to yourself?

Magical Moments:
(moments/people/experiences)

Intention you'd like to take into sleep with you?

MUSINGS · POPPED UP · REMEMBER · THINK · DOODLE · INNOVATE

Brevity is the soul of wit.
WILLIAM SHAKESPEARE

DATE ____ / ____ / 20____   O O O O O O O
                             S M T W TH F S

GETTING STARTED

I am grateful for:

MARGIN
MADNESS

Today's intention (in a word):

Supporting behavior(s):

WRAPPING UP

So, how did your day go? ☹ 😐 🙂 😊
What's your high-five to yourself?

Magical Moments:
(moments/people/experiences)

Intention you'd like to take into sleep with you?

MUSINGS · POPPED UP · REMEMBER · THINK · DOODLE · INNOVATE

Tears are the summer showers to the soul.
ALFRED AUSTIN

DATE ____ / ____ / 20___

○ ○ ○ ○ ○ ○ ○
S M T W TH F S

GETTING STARTED

I am grateful for:

Today's intention (in a word):

MARGIN
MADNESS

Supporting behavior(s):

WRAPPING UP

So, how did your day go? ☹ 😐 🙂 😊

What's your high-five to yourself?

Magical Moments:
(moments/people/experiences)

Intention you'd like to take into sleep with you?

MUSINGS · POPPED UP · REMEMBER · THINK · DOODLE · INNOVATE

If you have only one smile in you, give it to the people you love.

MAYA ANGELOU

DATE ____ / ____ / 20____

○ ○ ○ ○ ○ ○ ○
S M T W TH F S

GETTING STARTED

I am grateful for:

MARGIN MADNESS

Today's intention (in a word):

Supporting behavior(s):

WRAPPING UP

So, how did your day go? ☹ 😐 🙂 😊

What's your high-five to yourself?

Magical Moments:
(moments/people/experiences)

Intention you'd like to take into sleep with you?

INNOVATE · DOODLE · THINK · REMEMBER · POPPED UP · MUSINGS

No culture can live if it attempts to be exclusive.

MAHATMA GANDHI

DATE _____ / _____ / 20_____

○ ○ ○ ○ ○ ○ ○
S M T W TH F S

GETTING STARTED

I am grateful for:

Today's intention (in a word):

Supporting behavior(s):

WRAPPING UP

So, how did your day go? ☹ 😐 🙂 😊

What's your high-five to yourself?

Magical Moments:
(moments/people/experiences)

Intention you'd like to take into sleep with you?

I keep my heart and my soul and my spirit open to miracles.
PATRICK SWAYZE

DATE ____ / ____ / 20____

○ ○ ○ ○ ○ ○ ○
S M T W TH F S

GETTING STARTED

I am grateful for:

MARGIN
MADNESS

Today's intention (in a word):

Supporting behavior(s):

WRAPPING UP

So, how did your day go? ☹ 😐 🙂 😊

What's your high-five to yourself?

Magical Moments:
(moments/people/experiences)

Intention you'd like to take into sleep with you?

MUSINGS · POPPED UP · REMEMBER · THINK · DOODLE · INNOVATE

Gratitude in Action

Why fit in when you were born to stand out?
DR. SEUSS

Write down your superpower, and share it with two people. Be brave—allow your soul to shine in the light. The world needs you and your super power.

ACTION TAKEN:	FEELINGS EXPERIENCED:
THINGS LEARNED/ OBSERVED:	**WOULD I DO THIS AGAIN? WHY?**

Dreams are illustrations from the book your soul is writing about you.

MARSHA NORMAN

DATE ____ / ____ / 20____   O   O   O   O   O   O   O
                                    S   M   T   W   TH F   S

GETTING STARTED

I am grateful for:

MARGIN
MADNESS

Today's intention (in a word):

Supporting behavior(s):

INNOVATE · DOODLE · THINK · REMEMBER · POPPED UP · MUSINGS

WRAPPING UP

So, how did your day go?   ☹   😐   🙂   😊

What's your high-five to yourself?

Magical Moments:
(moments/people/experiences)

Intention you'd like to take into sleep with you?

Meditation is the soul's perspective glass.

OWEN FELTHAM

DATE ____ / ____ / 20____

○ ○ ○ ○ ○ ○ ○
S M T W TH F S

GETTING STARTED

I am grateful for:

Today's intention (in a word):

Supporting behavior(s):

MARGIN
MADNESS

WRAPPING UP

So, how did your day go? ☹ 😐 🙂 😊

What's your high-five to yourself?

Magical Moments:
(moments/people/experiences)

Intention you'd like to take into sleep with you?

MUSINGS · POPPED UP · REMEMBER · THINK · DOODLE · INNOVATE

*Spiritual relationship is far more precious than physical.
Physical relationship divorced from spiritual is body
without soul.*

MAHATMA GANDHI

DATE ____ / ____ / 20____

O O O O O O O
S M T W TH F S

GETTING STARTED

I am grateful for:

MARGIN
MADNESS

Today's intention (in a word):

Supporting behavior(s):

WRAPPING UP

So, how did your day go? ☹ 😐 🙂 😃

What's your high-five to yourself?

Magical Moments:
(moments/people/experiences)

Intention you'd like to take into sleep with you?

MUSINGS · POPPED UP · REMEMBER · THINK · DOODLE · INNOVATE

May my soul bloom in love for all existence.

RUDOLF STEINER

DATE _____ / _____ / 20_____

O O O O O O O
S M T W TH F S

GETTING STARTED

I am grateful for:

Today's intention (in a word):

Supporting behavior(s):

MARGIN
MADNESS

WRAPPING UP

So, how did your day go? ☹ 😐 🙂 😊

What's your high-five to yourself?

Magical Moments:
(moments/people/experiences)

Intention you'd like to take into sleep with you?

MUSINGS · POPPED UP · REMEMBER · THINK · DOODLE · INNOVATE

*Start by doing whats necessary, then do what's possible,
and suddenly you are doing the impossible.*

FRANCIS OF ASSISI

DATE ____ / ____ / 20____

○ ○ ○ ○ ○ ○ ○
S M T W TH F S

GETTING STARTED

I am grateful for:

MARGIN
MADNESS

Today's intention (in a word):

Supporting behavior(s):

INNOVATE · DOODLE · THINK · REMEMBER · POPPED UP · MUSINGS

WRAPPING UP

So, how did your day go? ☹ 😐 🙂 😊

What's your high-five to yourself?

Magical Moments:
(moments/people/experiences)

Intention you'd like to take into sleep with you?

We know what we are, but know not what we may be.

WILLIAM SHAKESPEARE

DATE ____ / ____ / 20____

○ ○ ○ ○ ○ ○ ○
S M T W TH F S

GETTING STARTED

I am grateful for:

Today's intention (in a word):

Supporting behavior(s):

WRAPPING UP

So, how did your day go? ☹ 😐 🙂 😊

What's your high-five to yourself?

Magical Moments:
(moments/people/experiences)

Intention you'd like to take into sleep with you?

Gratitude in Action

Our lives begin to end the day we become silent about things that matter.

DR. MARTIN LUTHER KING, JR.

List three things you STAND for, and find a way to contribute to them.

ACTION TAKEN:	FEELINGS EXPERIENCED:
THINGS LEARNED/ OBSERVED:	**WOULD I DO THIS AGAIN? WHY?**

There are two ways of spreading light: to be the candle or the mirror that reflects it.

EDITH WHARTON

DATE ____ / ____ / 20____

○ ○ ○ ○ ○ ○ ○
S M T W TH F S

GETTING STARTED

I am grateful for:

Today's intention (in a word):

MARGIN
MADNESS

Supporting behavior(s):

WRAPPING UP

So, how did your day go? ☹ 😐 🙂 😊

What's your high-five to yourself?

Magical Moments:
(moments/people/experiences)

Intention you'd like to take into sleep with you?

MUSINGS · POPPED UP · REMEMBER · THINK · DOODLE · INNOVATE

Throw your dreams into space like a kite, and you do not know what it will bring back: a new life, a new friend, a new love, a new country.

ANAIS NIN

DATE ____ / ____ / 20____

○ ○ ○ ○ ○ ○ ○
S M T W TH F S

GETTING STARTED

I am grateful for:

MARGIN
MADNESS

Today's intention (in a word):

Supporting behavior(s):

WRAPPING UP

So, how did your day go? ☹ 😐 😊 ☺

What's your high-five to yourself?

Magical Moments:
(moments/people/experiences)

Intention you'd like to take into sleep with you?

INNOVATE · DOODLE · THINK · REMEMBER · POPPED UP · MUSINGS

There is nothing impossible to him who will try.

ALEXANDER THE GREAT

DATE ____ / ____ / 20____

○ ○ ○ ○ ○ ○ ○
S M T W TH F S

GETTING STARTED

I am grateful for:

Today's intention (in a word):

MARGIN
MADNESS

Supporting behavior(s):

WRAPPING UP

So, how did your day go? ☹ ☹ ☺ ☺

What's your high-five to yourself?

Magical Moments:
(moments/people/experiences)

Intention you'd like to take into sleep with you?

MUSINGS · POPPED UP · REMEMBER · THINK · DOODLE · INNOVATE

*If we did all the things we are capable of, we would
literally astound ourselves.*

THOMAS EDISON

DATE ___ / ___ / 20___   O O O O O O O
                                S M T W TH F S

GETTING STARTED

I am grateful for:

MARGIN
MADNESS

Today's intention (in a word):

Supporting behavior(s):

WRAPPING UP

So, how did your day go? ☹ ☹ ☺ ☺

What's your high-five to yourself?

Magical Moments:
(moments/people/experiences)

Intention you'd like to take into sleep with you?

MUSINGS · POPPED UP · REMEMBER · THINK · DOODLE · INNOVATE

There must be quite a few things a hot bath won't cure,
but I don't know many of them.

SYLVIA PLATH

DATE _____ / _____ / 20_____

○ ○ ○ ○ ○ ○ ○
S M T W TH F S

GETTING STARTED

I am grateful for:

Today's intention (in a word):

MARGIN
MADNESS

Supporting behavior(s):

WRAPPING UP

So, how did your day go? ☹ 😐 🙂 😊

What's your high-five to yourself?

Magical Moments:
(moments/people/experiences)

Intention you'd like to take into sleep with you?

MUSINGS · POPPED UP · REMEMBER · THINK · DOODLE · INNOVATE

In the silence of the mountain, there is much you can learn.

DENNIS MCKAY

DATE ____ / ____ / 20____

○ ○ ○ ○ ○ ○ ○
S M T W TH F S

GETTING STARTED

I am grateful for:

MARGIN
MADNESS

Today's intention (in a word):

Supporting behavior(s):

INNOVATE · DOODLE · THINK · REMEMBER · POPPED UP · MUSINGS

WRAPPING UP

So, how did your day go? ☹ 😐 🙂 😊

What's your high-five to yourself?

Magical Moments:
(moments/people/experiences)

Intention you'd like to take into sleep with you?

Make the most of yourself, for that is all there is of you.

RALPH WALDO EMERSON

DATE ____ / ____ / 20____

○ ○ ○ ○ ○ ○ ○
S M T W TH F S

GETTING STARTED

I am grateful for:

Today's intention (in a word):

Supporting behavior(s):

MARGIN
MADNESS

WRAPPING UP

So, how did your day go? ☹ 😐 🙂 😊

What's your high-five to yourself?

Magical Moments:
(moments/people/experiences)

Intention you'd like to take into sleep with you?

MUSINGS · POPPED UP · REMEMBER · THINK · DOODLE · INNOVATE

HELLO AGAIN

Here is some quick inspiration for you.

In 2006, I was a few years into my gratitude practice and had been consistent for close to nine consecutive months. I was feeling the strain of owning a home and everything that comes with it. One particular morning, I grabbed my journal, an amazingly aromatic cup of coffee, and found a cozy place to sit.

I remember feeling thankful for a sharp pencil, the author that created the journal I was using, the soft comfy couch I was sitting on inside my warm, safe home. I instantly felt relief from all the bills and stress—in one moment of gratitude my home was no longer the burden I had seen it as. I am not sure how to explain the freedom I experienced in that moment except to say it was profound.

It was simple—no lights flashing, no billboards, yet that moment was life changing and a gift inside the practice of gratitude.

This is just the beginning...enjoy your day!

What are you noticing about your life and our world that may have previously been passing you by?

Gratitude in Action

Journeying is a lifestyle change.
S KELLEY HARRELL

Think about your journaling journey. Reflect on how it has changed your life—it doesn't have to be earth-shattering. No billboards or flashing lights required.

ACTION TAKEN:	FEELINGS EXPERIENCED:
THINGS LEARNED/ OBSERVED:	**WOULD I DO THIS AGAIN? WHY?**

How wonderful it is that nobody need wait a single moment before starting to improve the world.

ANNE FRANK

DATE ____ / ____ / 20____

○ ○ ○ ○ ○ ○ ○
S M T W TH F S

GETTING STARTED

I am grateful for:

MARGIN
MADNESS

Today's intention (in a word):

Supporting behavior(s):

WRAPPING UP

So, how did your day go? ☹ 😐 🙂 😊

What's your high-five to yourself?

Magical Moments:
(moments/people/experiences)

Intention you'd like to take into sleep with you?

MUSINGS · POPPED UP · REMEMBER · THINK · DOODLE · INNOVATE

Nowhere can man find a quieter or more untroubled retreat than in his soul.

MARCUS AURELIUS

DATE _____ / _____ / 20_____

O O O O O O O
S M T W TH F S

GETTING STARTED

I am grateful for:

Today's intention (in a word):

MARGIN
MADNESS

Supporting behavior(s):

WRAPPING UP

So, how did your day go? ☹ 😐 🙂 😊

What's your high-five to yourself?

Magical Moments:
(moments/people/experiences)

Intention you'd like to take into sleep with you?

MUSINGS · POPPED UP · REMEMBER · THINK · DOODLE · INNOVATE

Believe you can and you're halfway there.

THEODORE ROOSEVELT

DATE _____ / _____ / 20_____

○ ○ ○ ○ ○ ○ ○
S M T W TH F S

GETTING STARTED

I am grateful for:

MARGIN MADNESS

Today's intention (in a word):

Supporting behavior(s):

WRAPPING UP

So, how did your day go?   ☹ 😐 🙂 😊

What's your high-five to yourself?

Magical Moments:
(moments/people/experiences)

Intention you'd like to take into sleep with you?

INNOVATE · DOODLE · THINK · REMEMBER · POPPED UP · MUSINGS

If opportunity doesn't knock, build a door.

MILTON BERLE

DATE _____ / _____ / 20_____

O O O O O O O
S M T W TH F S

GETTING STARTED

I am grateful for:

Today's intention (in a word):

MARGIN
MADNESS

Supporting behavior(s):

WRAPPING UP

So, how did your day go? ☹ 😐 🙂 😊

What's your high-five to yourself?

Magical Moments:
(moments/people/experiences)

Intention you'd like to take into sleep with you?

MUSINGS · POPPED UP · REMEMBER · THINK · DOODLE · INNOVATE

The things that we love tell us what we are.
THOMAS AQUINAS

DATE ____ / ____ / 20____

○ ○ ○ ○ ○ ○ ○
S M T W TH F S

GETTING STARTED

I am grateful for:

MARGIN
MADNESS

Today's intention (in a word):

Supporting behavior(s):

MUSINGS · POPPED UP · REMEMBER · THINK · DOODLE · INNOVATE

WRAPPING UP

So, how did your day go? ☹ 😐 😃 😊

What's your high-five to yourself?

Magical Moments:
(moments/people/experiences)

Intention you'd like to take into sleep with you?

Grace is the beauty of form under the influence of freedom.

FRIEDRICH SCHILLER

DATE ____ / ____ / 20____   O O O O O O O
                                    S M T W TH F S

GETTING STARTED

I am grateful for:

Today's intention (in a word):

Supporting behavior(s):

MARGIN
MADNESS

WRAPPING UP

So, how did your day go?   ☹ 😐 😀 🙂

What's your high-five to yourself?

Magical Moments:
(moments/people/experiences)

Intention you'd like to take into sleep with you?

MUSINGS · POPPED UP · REMEMBER · THINK · DOODLE · INNOVATE

> *When he worked, he really worked. But when he played, he really played.*
> DR. SEUSS

DATE ____ / ____ / 20____

○ ○ ○ ○ ○ ○ ○
S M T W TH F S

GETTING STARTED

I am grateful for:

MARGIN
MADNESS

Today's intention (in a word):

Supporting behavior(s):

WRAPPING UP

So, how did your day go? ☹ 😐 🙂 😊

What's your high-five to yourself?

Magical Moments:
(moments/people/experiences)

Intention you'd like to take into sleep with you?

MUSINGS · POPPED UP · REMEMBER · THINK · DOODLE · INNOVATE

When the whole world is silent, even one voice becomes powerful.

MALALA YOUSAFZAI

DATE ____ / ____ / 20____   ○ ○ ○ ○ ○ ○ ○
                            S M T W TH F S

GETTING STARTED

I am grateful for:

Today's intention (in a word):

Supporting behavior(s):

MARGIN
MADNESS

WRAPPING UP

So, how did your day go? ☹ 😐 😀 😊

What's your high-five to yourself?

Magical Moments:
(moments/people/experiences)

Intention you'd like to take into sleep with you?

MUSINGS · POPPED UP · REMEMBER · THINK · DOODLE · INNOVATE

Gratitude in Action

If no one is smiling at you, check your reflection.

AUTHOR UNKNOWN

Make a point today to smile at more than eleven strangers. Yes, you are actually counting smiles—enjoy!

ACTION TAKEN:	FEELINGS EXPERIENCED:
THINGS LEARNED/ OBSERVED:	**WOULD I DO THIS AGAIN? WHY?**

> *All your questions will be answered, if that is what you want. But once you learn the answers, you can never unlearn them.*
>
> NEIL GAIMAN

DATE _____ / _____ / 20_____

○ ○ ○ ○ ○ ○ ○
S M T W TH F S

GETTING STARTED

I am grateful for:

Today's intention (in a word):

MARGIN
MADNESS

Supporting behavior(s):

WRAPPING UP

So, how did your day go? ☹ 😐 🙂 😊

What's your high-five to yourself?

Magical Moments:
(moments/people/experiences)

Intention you'd like to take into sleep with you?

MUSINGS · POPPED UP · REMEMBER · THINK · DOODLE · INNOVATE

If you are not the hero of your own novel, then what kind of novel is it? You need to do some heavy editing.

TERENCE MCKENNA

DATE ____ / ____ / 20____   S M T W TH F S

GETTING STARTED

I am grateful for:

MARGIN
MADNESS

Today's intention (in a word):

Supporting behavior(s):

MUSINGS · POPPED UP · REMEMBER · THINK · DOODLE · INNOVATE

WRAPPING UP

So, how did your day go? ☹ 😐 🙂 😊

What's your high-five to yourself?

Magical Moments:
(moments/people/experiences)

Intention you'd like to take into sleep with you?

Sophistication is the art of dancing with one's own imperfections.

ALEXSYS THOMPSON

DATE _____ / _____ / 20_____   ○ ○ ○ ○ ○ ○ ○
                                 S M T W TH F S

GETTING STARTED

I am grateful for:

Today's intention (in a word):

Supporting behavior(s):

MARGIN
MADNESS

WRAPPING UP

So, how did your day go? ☹ 😐 🙂 😊

What's your high-five to yourself?

Magical Moments:
(moments/people/experiences)

Intention you'd like to take into sleep with you?

MUSINGS · POPPED UP · REMEMBER · THINK · DOODLE · INNOVATE

It takes courage to grow up and become who you really are.

E.E. CUMMINGS

DATE ____ / ____ / 20____   ○ ○ ○ ○ ○ ○ ○
                              S M T W TH F S

GETTING STARTED

I am grateful for:

MARGIN
MADNESS

Today's intention (in a word):

Supporting behavior(s):

WRAPPING UP

So, how did your day go?   ☹ 😐 😀 😊
What's your high-five to yourself?

Magical Moments:
(moments/people/experiences)

Intention you'd like to take into sleep with you?

MUSINGS · POPPED UP · REMEMBER · THINK · DOODLE · INNOVATE

*Only those that will risk going too far can possibly find
out how far we can go.*

T.S. ELIOT

DATE ____ / ____ / 20____

○ ○ ○ ○ ○ ○ ○
S M T W TH F S

GETTING STARTED

I am grateful for:

Today's intention (in a word):

MARGIN
MADNESS

Supporting behavior(s):

WRAPPING UP

So, how did your day go? ☹ 😐 🙂 😊

What's your high-five to yourself?

Magical Moments:
(moments/people/experiences)

Intention you'd like to take into sleep with you?

MUSINGS • POPPED UP • REMEMBER • THINK • DOODLE • INNOVATE

The mind is a place where the soul goes to hide from the heart.

MICHAEL SINGER

DATE ____ / ____ / 20____

○ ○ ○ ○ ○ ○ ○
S M T W TH F S

GETTING STARTED

I am grateful for:

MARGIN
MADNESS

Today's intention (in a word):

Supporting behavior(s):

MUSINGS · POPPED UP · REMEMBER · THINK · DOODLE · INNOVATE

WRAPPING UP

So, how did your day go? ☹ 😐 😊 ☺

What's your high-five to yourself?

Magical Moments:
(moments/people/experiences)

Intention you'd like to take into sleep with you?

Sometimes things fall apart so that better things can fall together.

MARILYN MONROE

DATE _____ / _____ / 20_____

○ ○ ○ ○ ○ ○ ○
S M T W TH F S

GETTING STARTED

I am grateful for:

Today's intention (in a word):

Supporting behavior(s):

MARGIN
MADNESS

WRAPPING UP

So, how did your day go? ☹ 😐 😀 🙂

What's your high-five to yourself?

Magical Moments:
(moments/people/experiences)

Intention you'd like to take into sleep with you?

MUSINGS · POPPED UP · REMEMBER · THINK · DOODLE · INNOVATE

Even if I knew that tomorrow the world would go to pieces, I would still plant my apple tree.

MARTIN LUTHER

DATE ____ / ____ / 20____

○ ○ ○ ○ ○ ○ ○
S M T W TH F S

GETTING STARTED

I am grateful for:

MARGIN
MADNESS

Today's intention (in a word):

Supporting behavior(s):

WRAPPING UP

So, how did your day go? ☹ 😐 🙂 😊

What's your high-five to yourself?

Magical Moments:
(moments/people/experiences)

Intention you'd like to take into sleep with you?

INNOVATE · DOODLE · THINK · REMEMBER · POPPED UP · MUSINGS

Gratitude in Action

I would rather fail on my own terms than succeed by those of another.

AUTHOR UNKNOWN

Jot down a recent failure and the learning that came from it.

ACTION TAKEN:	FEELINGS EXPERIENCED:
THINGS LEARNED/ OBSERVED:	**WOULD I DO THIS AGAIN? WHY?**

The best way to cheer yourself up is to cheer somebody else up.

ALBERT EINSTEIN

DATE _____ / _____ / 20_____

○ ○ ○ ○ ○ ○ ○
S M T W TH F S

GETTING STARTED

I am grateful for:

MARGIN
MADNESS

Today's intention (in a word):

Supporting behavior(s):

INNOVATE · DOODLE · THINK · REMEMBER · POPPED UP · MUSINGS

WRAPPING UP

So, how did your day go? ☹ 😐 😊 😄

What's your high-five to yourself?

Magical Moments:
(moments/people/experiences)

Intention you'd like to take into sleep with you?

Make sure your worst enemy doesn't live between your own two ears.

LAIRD HAMILTON

DATE _____ / _____ / 20_____

○ ○ ○ ○ ○ ○ ○
S M T W TH F S

GETTING STARTED

I am grateful for:

Today's intention (in a word):

Supporting behavior(s):

MARGIN
MADNESS

WRAPPING UP

So, how did your day go? ☹ 😐 🙂 😊

What's your high-five to yourself?

Magical Moments:
(moments/people/experiences)

Intention you'd like to take into sleep with you?

MUSINGS · POPPED UP · REMEMBER · THINK · DOODLE · INNOVATE

The universe buries strange jewels deep within us all,
and then stands back to see if we can find them.
ELIZABETH GILBERT

DATE ____ / ____ / 20____

O O O O O O O
S M T W TH F S

GETTING STARTED

I am grateful for:

MARGIN
MADNESS

Today's intention (in a word):

Supporting behavior(s):

INNOVATE · DOODLE · THINK · REMEMBER · POPPED UP · MUSINGS

WRAPPING UP

So, how did your day go? ☹ 😐 🙂 😊
What's your high-five to yourself?

Magical Moments:
(moments/people/experiences)

Intention you'd like to take into sleep with you?

Love all, trust a few, do wrong to none.
WILLIAM SHAKESPEARE

DATE ____ / ____ / 20____

○ ○ ○ ○ ○ ○ ○
S M T W TH F S

GETTING STARTED

I am grateful for:

Today's intention (in a word):

Supporting behavior(s):

MARGIN
MADNESS

WRAPPING UP

So, how did your day go? ☹ 😐 🙂 😊

What's your high-five to yourself?

Magical Moments:
(moments/people/experiences)

Intention you'd like to take into sleep with you?

MUSINGS · POPPED UP · REMEMBER · THINK · DOODLE · INNOVATE

The measure of who we are is what we do with what we have.

VINCE LOMBARDI

DATE ____ / ____ / 20____

○ ○ ○ ○ ○ ○ ○
S M T W TH F S

GETTING STARTED

I am grateful for:

MARGIN
MADNESS

Today's intention (in a word):

Supporting behavior(s):

WRAPPING UP

So, how did your day go? ☹ 😐 🙂 😊

What's your high-five to yourself?

Magical Moments:
(moments/people/experiences)

Intention you'd like to take into sleep with you?

MUSINGS · POPPED UP · REMEMBER · THINK · DOODLE · INNOVATE

At the end of the game, the king and the pawn go back in the same box.

ITALIC PROVERB

DATE _____ / _____ / 20_____

○ ○ ○ ○ ○ ○ ○
S M T W TH F S

GETTING STARTED

I am grateful for:

Today's intention (in a word):

MARGIN
MADNESS

Supporting behavior(s):

WRAPPING UP

So, how did your day go? ☹ 😐 🙂 😊

What's your high-five to yourself?

Magical Moments:
(moments/people/experiences)

Intention you'd like to take into sleep with you?

MUSINGS · POPPED UP · REMEMBER · THINK · DOODLE · INNOVATE

Gratitude in Action

I only feel angry when I see waste. When I see people throwing away things we could use.
MOTHER THERESA

Take something you have and do not need, and give it to somone who does.

ACTION TAKEN:	FEELINGS EXPERIENCED:
THINGS LEARNED/ OBSERVED:	WOULD I DO THIS AGAIN? WHY?

As knowledge increases, wonder deepens.

CHARLES MORGAN

DATE ____ / ____ / 20____

○ ○ ○ ○ ○ ○ ○
S M T W TH F S

GETTING STARTED

I am grateful for:

Today's intention (in a word):

MARGIN
MADNESS

Supporting behavior(s):

WRAPPING UP

So, how did your day go? 😞 😐 🙂 😊

What's your high-five to yourself?

Magical Moments:
(moments/people/experiences)

Intention you'd like to take into sleep with you?

MUSINGS · POPPED UP · REMEMBER · THINK · DOODLE · INNOVATE

Find out who you are and be that person. That's what your soul was put on this Earth to be. Find the truth, live that truth and everything else will come.

ELLEN DEGENERES

DATE ____ / ____ / 20____   ○ ○ ○ ○ ○ ○ ○
                              S M T W TH F S

GETTING STARTED

I am grateful for:

MARGIN
MADNESS

Today's intention (in a word):

Supporting behavior(s):

WRAPPING UP

So, how did your day go? ☹ 😐 🙂 😊

What's your high-five to yourself?

Magical Moments:
(moments/people/experiences)

Intention you'd like to take into sleep with you?

MUSINGS · POPPED UP · REMEMBER · THINK · DOODLE · INNOVATE

HOW EXCITING

It's so good to see you here. Your gratitude practice is moving along nicely!

Today I would like to share the gift of connectedness. At this point, I am hoping you are starting to see that *one thing* is connected to *all things*.

In 2007, I had a run-in with Bell's Palsy. If you haven't heard of it, it's a condition where the muscles in half your face become weak or paralyzed. The left side of my face was drooping, I was drooling and couldn't shut my left eye—all things I took for granted before this experience.

Have you ever thanked your eye for shutting or your mouth for closing to keep drinks and food in? I do now, daily.

Our bodies are temples we contaminate and take for granted every day. Thank your eyes for the ability to read this text!

This experience was so full of gifts. Most importantly, I now have internal signs I need rest. When I have a numbing feeling in my face or my eye starts to sag, I (and my loved ones) know I need to take a break. I am grateful for the signs and the people who understand how to help me be who I say I want to be.

Can you see all the threads connecting me to my body, me to my word, my loved ones seeing me? Fun, isn't it?

Once you make a decision, the universe conspires to make it happen.

RALPH WALDO EMERSON

DATE ____ / ____ / 20____   ○ ○ ○ ○ ○ ○ ○
                             S M T W TH F S

GETTING STARTED

I am grateful for:

MARGIN
MADNESS

Today's intention (in a word):

Supporting behavior(s):

WRAPPING UP

So, how did your day go? ☹ 😐 🙂 😊

What's your high-five to yourself?

Magical Moments:
(moments/people/experiences)

Intention you'd like to take into sleep with you?

MUSINGS · POPPED UP · REMEMBER · THINK · DOODLE · INNOVATE

A joy that isn't shared dies young.
ANNE SEXTON

DATE ____ / ____ / 20____

O O O O O O O
S M T W TH F S

GETTING STARTED

I am grateful for:

Today's intention (in a word):

Supporting behavior(s):

MARGIN
MADNESS

WRAPPING UP

So, how did your day go? ☹ 😕 🙂 😊

What's your high-five to yourself?

Magical Moments:
(moments/people/experiences)

Intention you'd like to take into sleep with you?

MUSINGS · POPPED UP · REMEMBER · THINK · DOODLE · INNOVATE

*Your work is to discover your world and then, with all
your heart, give yourself to it.*
BUDDHA

DATE ____ / ____ / 20____

○ ○ ○ ○ ○ ○ ○
S M T W TH F S

GETTING STARTED

I am grateful for:

MARGIN
MADNESS

Today's intention (in a word):

Supporting behavior(s):

WRAPPING UP

So, how did your day go? ☹ 😐 😊 😄

What's your high-five to yourself?

Magical Moments:
(moments/people/experiences)

Intention you'd like to take into sleep with you?

INNOVATE · DOODLE · THINK · REMEMBER · POPPED UP · MUSINGS

Just because it didn't last forever, doesn't mean it wasn't worth your while.

AUTHOR UNKNOWN

DATE ____ / ____ / 20___

○ ○ ○ ○ ○ ○ ○
S M T W TH F S

GETTING STARTED

I am grateful for:

Today's intention (in a word):

Supporting behavior(s):

MARGIN
MADNESS

WRAPPING UP

So, how did your day go? ☹ 😐 😊 ☺

What's your high-five to yourself?

Magical Moments:
(moments/people/experiences)

Intention you'd like to take into sleep with you?

MUSINGS · POPPED UP · REMEMBER · THINK · DOODLE · INNOVATE

Speak when you are angry and you will make the best speech you will ever regret.

AMBROSE BIERCE

DATE ____ / ____ / 20____

○ ○ ○ ○ ○ ○ ○
S M T W TH F S

GETTING STARTED

I am grateful for:

MARGIN
MADNESS

Today's intention (in a word):

Supporting behavior(s):

WRAPPING UP

So, how did your day go? ☹ 😐 🙂 😊

What's your high-five to yourself?

Magical Moments:
(moments/people/experiences)

Intention you'd like to take into sleep with you?

INNOVATE · DOODLE · THINK · REMEMBER · POPPED UP · MUSINGS

Gratitude in Action

Even the upper end of the river believes in the ocean.
WILLIAM STAFFORD

Ponder some of the things you have faith in that you cannot see or understand.

ACTION TAKEN:	FEELINGS EXPERIENCED:
THINGS LEARNED/ OBSERVED:	**WOULD I DO THIS AGAIN? WHY?**

Put down your baggage my friend and come on in.
ALEXSYS THOMPSON

DATE ____ / ____ / 20____   O O O O O O O
                              S M T W TH F S

GETTING STARTED

I am grateful for:

MARGIN
MADNESS

Today's intention (in a word):

Supporting behavior(s):

WRAPPING UP

So, how did your day go?   ☹ 😐 🙂 😊

What's your high-five to yourself?

Magical Moments:
(moments/people/experiences)

Intention you'd like to take into sleep with you?

MUSINGS · POPPED UP · REMEMBER · THINK · DOODLE · INNOVATE

Death is only the end if you assume the story is about you.
JOSEPH FINK

DATE ____ / ____ / 20____   ○ ○ ○ ○ ○ ○ ○
                                 S M T W TH F S

GETTING STARTED

I am grateful for:

Today's intention (in a word):

MARGIN
MADNESS

Supporting behavior(s):

WRAPPING UP

So, how did your day go? ☹ 😐 🙂 😊

What's your high-five to yourself?

Magical Moments:
(moments/people/experiences)

Intention you'd like to take into sleep with you?

MUSINGS · POPPED UP · REMEMBER · THINK · DOODLE · INNOVATE

An individual has not started living until he can rise above the narrow confines of his individualistic concerns to the broader concerns of all humanity.

MARTIN LUTHER KING, JR.

DATE _____ / _____ / 20_____

○ ○ ○ ○ ○ ○ ○
S M T W TH F S

GETTING STARTED

I am grateful for:

MARGIN
MADNESS

Today's intention (in a word):

Supporting behavior(s):

WRAPPING UP

So, how did your day go? 😦 😐 🙂 😊
What's your high-five to yourself?

Magical Moments:
(moments/people/experiences)

Intention you'd like to take into sleep with you?

MUSINGS · POPPED UP · REMEMBER · THINK · DOODLE · INNOVATE

Life is the flower for which love is the honey.

VICTOR HUGO

DATE ____ / ____ / 20____

O O O O O O O
S M T W TH F S

GETTING STARTED

I am grateful for:

Today's intention (in a word):

Supporting behavior(s):

MARGIN
MADNESS

WRAPPING UP

So, how did your day go? ☹ 😐 🙂 😊

What's your high-five to yourself?

Magical Moments:
(moments/people/experiences)

Intention you'd like to take into sleep with you?

MUSINGS · POPPED UP · REMEMBER · THINK · DOODLE · INNOVATE

Keep away from people who try to belittle your ambitions. Small people always do that, but the really great make you feel that you, too, can become great."

MARK TWAIN

DATE ____ / ____ / 20____

○ ○ ○ ○ ○ ○ ○
S M T W TH F S

MARGIN MADNESS

GETTING STARTED

I am grateful for:

Today's intention (in a word):

Supporting behavior(s):

INNOVATE · DOODLE · THINK · REMEMBER · POPPED UP · MUSINGS

WRAPPING UP

So, how did your day go? ☹ 😐 🙂 😊

What's your high-five to yourself?

Magical Moments:
(moments/people/experiences)

Intention you'd like to take into sleep with you?

There is no love without forgiveness, and there is no forgiveness without love.

BRYANT H. MCGILL

DATE ____ / ____ / 20____

○ ○ ○ ○ ○ ○ ○
S M T W TH F S

GETTING STARTED

I am grateful for:

Today's intention (in a word):

MARGIN
MADNESS

Supporting behavior(s):

WRAPPING UP

So, how did your day go? ☹ 😐 🙂 😊

What's your high-five to yourself?

Magical Moments:
(moments/people/experiences)

Intention you'd like to take into sleep with you?

MUSINGS · POPPED UP · REMEMBER · THINK · DOODLE · INNOVATE

Gratitude in Action

When the flower blooms, the bees come uninvited.
EMMA GOLDMAN

Invite somone into your space, and share a part of your heart with them.

ACTION TAKEN:	FEELINGS EXPERIENCED:
THINGS LEARNED/ OBSERVED:	**WOULD I DO THIS AGAIN? WHY?**

You are the Universe expressing itself as a human for a little while.

ECKHART TOLLE

DATE ____ / ____ / 20____

○ ○ ○ ○ ○ ○ ○
S M T W TH F S

GETTING STARTED

I am grateful for:

Today's intention (in a word):

MARGIN
MADNESS

Supporting behavior(s):

WRAPPING UP

So, how did your day go? ☹ 😐 😊 🙂

What's your high-five to yourself?

Magical Moments:
(moments/people/experiences)

Intention you'd like to take into sleep with you?

MUSINGS · POPPED UP · REMEMBER · THINK · DOODLE · INNOVATE

Thousands of candles can be lighted from a single candle, and the life of the candle will not be shortened. Happiness never decreases by being shared.

BUDDHA

DATE ____ / ____ / 20____

○ ○ ○ ○ ○ ○ ○
S M T W TH F S

GETTING STARTED

I am grateful for:

MARGIN
MADNESS

Today's intention (in a word):

Supporting behavior(s):

INNOVATE · DOODLE · THINK · REMEMBER · POPPED UP · MUSINGS

WRAPPING UP

So, how did your day go? ☹ 😐 🙂 😊

What's your high-five to yourself?

Magical Moments:
(moments/people/experiences)

Intention you'd like to take into sleep with you?

Happiness is when what you think, what you say, and what you do are in harmony.

MAHATMA GANDHI

DATE ____ / ____ / 20____

O O O O O O O
S M T W TH F S

GETTING STARTED

I am grateful for:

Today's intention (in a word):

Supporting behavior(s):

MARGIN
MADNESS

WRAPPING UP

So, how did your day go? ☹ 😐 🙂 😊

What's your high-five to yourself?

Magical Moments:
(moments/people/experiences)

Intention you'd like to take into sleep with you?

MUSINGS · POPPED UP · REMEMBER · THINK · DOODLE · INNOVATE

What we call the beginning is often the end. And to make a end is to make a beginning. The end is where we start from.

T.S. ELIOT

DATE _____ / _____ / 20_____

○ ○ ○ ○ ○ ○ ○
S M T W TH F S

GETTING STARTED

I am grateful for:

MARGIN
MADNESS

Today's intention (in a word):

Supporting behavior(s):

WRAPPING UP

So, how did your day go? ☹ 😐 🙂 😊

What's your high-five to yourself?

Magical Moments:
(moments/people/experiences)

Intention you'd like to take into sleep with you?

MUSINGS · POPPED UP · REMEMBER · THINK · DOODLE · INNOVATE

As a body everyone is single, as a soul never.
HERMANN HESSE

DATE _____ / _____ / 20_____

○ ○ ○ ○ ○ ○ ○
S M T W TH F S

GETTING STARTED

I am grateful for:

Today's intention (in a word):

MARGIN
MADNESS

Supporting behavior(s):

WRAPPING UP

So, how did your day go? ☹ 😕 🙂 😊

What's your high-five to yourself?

Magical Moments:
(moments/people/experiences)

Intention you'd like to take into sleep with you?

MUSINGS · POPPED UP · REMEMBER · THINK · DOODLE · INNOVATE

The heart wants what it wants. There's no logic to these things. You meet someone, and you fall in love, and that's that.

WOODY ALLEN

DATE ____ / ____ / 20____

○ ○ ○ ○ ○ ○ ○
S M T W TH F S

GETTING STARTED

I am grateful for:

Today's intention (in a word):

Supporting behavior(s):

WRAPPING UP

So, how did your day go? ☹ 😐 🙂 😊

What's your high-five to yourself?

Magical Moments:
(moments/people/experiences)

Intention you'd like to take into sleep with you?

Possibility: everything that you could ever imagine, and nothing you can't.

UNKNOWN AUTHOR

DATE ____ / ____ / 20____

○ ○ ○ ○ ○ ○ ○
S M T W TH F S

GETTING STARTED

I am grateful for:

Today's intention (in a word):

MARGIN
MADNESS

Supporting behavior(s):

WRAPPING UP

So, how did your day go? ☹ 😐 🙂 😊

What's your high-five to yourself?

Magical Moments:
(moments/people/experiences)

Intention you'd like to take into sleep with you?

MUSINGS · POPPED UP · REMEMBER · THINK · DOODLE · INNOVATE

*Use the talents you possess, the woods will be very silent
if no birds sang except those that sang best.*

HENRY VAN DYKE

DATE ____ / ____ / 20____   ○ ○ ○ ○ ○ ○ ○
                             S M T W TH F S

GETTING STARTED

I am grateful for:

MARGIN
MADNESS

Today's intention (in a word):

Supporting behavior(s):

WRAPPING UP

So, how did your day go? ☹ 😐 🙂 😊

What's your high-five to yourself?

Magical Moments:
(moments/people/experiences)

Intention you'd like to take into sleep with you?

MUSINGS · POPPED UP · REMEMBER · THINK · DOODLE · INNOVATE

Gratitude in Action

What is not started today is never finished tomorrow.
DR. THERESA NICASSIO

Choose something you've been putting off, and get it started/done today. Share it with someone else to help you align your intentions and behaviors.

ACTION TAKEN:	FEELINGS EXPERIENCED:
THINGS LEARNED/ OBSERVED:	**WOULD I DO THIS AGAIN? WHY?**

Sometimes me think, "What is Friend?", and then me say, "Friend is someone to share the last cookie with."

COOKIE MONSTER

DATE ____ / ____ / 20____   ○ ○ ○ ○ ○ ○ ○
                            S M T W TH F S

GETTING STARTED

I am grateful for:

MARGIN
MADNESS

Today's intention (in a word):

Supporting behavior(s):

WRAPPING UP

So, how did your day go? ☹ 😐 🙂 ☺

What's your high-five to yourself?

Magical Moments:
(moments/people/experiences)

Intention you'd like to take into sleep with you?

MUSINGS · POPPED UP · REMEMBER · THINK · DOODLE · INNOVATE

Humility is not thinking less of yourself; it is thinking of yourself less.

C.S. LEWIS

DATE ____ / ____ / 20____

○ ○ ○ ○ ○ ○ ○
S M T W TH F S

GETTING STARTED

I am grateful for:

Today's intention (in a word):

MARGIN
MADNESS

Supporting behavior(s):

WRAPPING UP

So, how did your day go? ☹ 🙁 🙂 😊

What's your high-five to yourself?

Magical Moments:
(moments/people/experiences)

Intention you'd like to take into sleep with you?

MUSINGS · POPPED UP · REMEMBER · THINK · DOODLE · INNOVATE

Whoever is happy will make others happy.

ANNE FRANK

DATE ____ / ____ / 20____

○ ○ ○ ○ ○ ○ ○
S M T W TH F S

GETTING STARTED

I am grateful for:

MARGIN
MADNESS

Today's intention (in a word):

Supporting behavior(s):

INNOVATE · DOODLE · THINK · REMEMBER · POPPED UP · MUSINGS

WRAPPING UP

So, how did your day go? ☹ 😐 ☺ 😊

What's your high-five to yourself?

Magical Moments:
(moments/people/experiences)

Intention you'd like to take into sleep with you?

Ultimately, America's answer to the intolerant man is diversity.

ROBERT KENNEDY

DATE ____ / ____ / 20____

○ ○ ○ ○ ○ ○ ○
S M T W TH F S

GETTING STARTED

I am grateful for:

Today's intention (in a word):

MARGIN
MADNESS

Supporting behavior(s):

WRAPPING UP

So, how did your day go? ☹ 😐 🙂 😊

What's your high-five to yourself?

Magical Moments:
(moments/people/experiences)

Intention you'd like to take into sleep with you?

MUSINGS · POPPED UP · REMEMBER · THINK · DOODLE · INNOVATE

Happiness is not in the mere possession of money; it lies in the joy of achievement, in the thrill of creative effort.

FRANKLIN D. ROOSEVELT

DATE _____ / _____ / 20_____

○ ○ ○ ○ ○ ○ ○
S M T W TH F S

GETTING STARTED

I am grateful for:

MARGIN
MADNESS

Today's intention (in a word):

Supporting behavior(s):

WRAPPING UP

So, how did your day go? ☹ 😐 🙂 😊

What's your high-five to yourself?

Magical Moments:
(moments/people/experiences)

Intention you'd like to take into sleep with you?

MUSINGS · POPPED UP · REMEMBER · THINK · DOODLE · INNOVATE

It matters not what someone is born, but what they grow to be.

JK ROWLING

DATE _____ / _____ / 20_____   ○ ○ ○ ○ ○ ○ ○
                                 S M T W TH F S

GETTING STARTED

I am grateful for:

Today's intention (in a word):

Supporting behavior(s):

WRAPPING UP

So, how did your day go? ☹ 😐 🙂 😊

What's your high-five to yourself?

Magical Moments:
(moments/people/experiences)

Intention you'd like to take into sleep with you?

Gratitude in Action

Do not spoil what you have by desiring what you have not; remember that what you now have was once among the things you only hoped for.

EPICURUS

Think back to a year ago: what do you have now and/ or have experienced now that you did not then? Do the same for three and five years ago. Let the joy of witnessing your journey in.

ACTION TAKEN:	FEELINGS EXPERIENCED:
THINGS LEARNED/ OBSERVED:	**WOULD I DO THIS AGAIN? WHY?**

Make your life spectacular. I know I did.
ROBIN WILLIAMS

DATE _____ / _____ / 20_____

○ ○ ○ ○ ○ ○ ○
S M T W TH F S

GETTING STARTED

I am grateful for:

Today's intention (in a word):

Supporting behavior(s):

MARGIN
MADNESS

WRAPPING UP

So, how did your day go? ☹ 😐 🙂 😊

What's your high-five to yourself?

Magical Moments:
(moments/people/experiences)

Intention you'd like to take into sleep with you?

MUSINGS · POPPED UP · REMEMBER · THINK · DOODLE · INNOVATE

If we couldn't laugh, we would all go insane.
ROBERT FROST

DATE ____ / ____ / 20____   ○ ○ ○ ○ ○ ○ ○
                               S M T W TH F S

GETTING STARTED

I am grateful for:

MARGIN
MADNESS

Today's intention (in a word):

Supporting behavior(s):

WRAPPING UP

So, how did your day go? ☹ ☹ ☺ ☺

What's your high-five to yourself?

Magical Moments:
(moments/people/experiences)

Intention you'd like to take into sleep with you?

MUSINGS · POPPED UP · REMEMBER · THINK · DOODLE · INNOVATE

If you are tired, keep going; if you are scared, keep going; if you are hungry; keep going; if you want to taste freedom, keep going.

HARRIET TUBMAN

DATE ____ / ____ / 20____   ○ ○ ○ ○ ○ ○ ○
                             S M T W TH F S

GETTING STARTED

I am grateful for:

Today's intention (in a word):

Supporting behavior(s):

MARGIN
MADNESS

WRAPPING UP

So, how did your day go? ☹ 😐 🙂 😊

What's your high-five to yourself?

Magical Moments:
(moments/people/experiences)

Intention you'd like to take into sleep with you?

MUSINGS · POPPED UP · REMEMBER · THINK · DOODLE · INNOVATE

Passion is energy. Feel the power that comes from focusing on what excites you.
OPRAH

DATE ____ / ____ / 20____   ○ ○ ○ ○ ○ ○ ○
                            S M T W TH F S

GETTING STARTED

I am grateful for:

MARGIN
MADNESS

Today's intention (in a word):

Supporting behavior(s):

INNOVATE · DOODLE · THINK · REMEMBER · POPPED UP · MUSINGS

WRAPPING UP

So, how did your day go?   ☹ 😐 🙂 😊

What's your high-five to yourself?

Magical Moments:
(moments/people/experiences)

Intention you'd like to take into sleep with you?

Humility stands wise while ego stumbles with pride.

AUTHOR UNKNOWN

DATE ____ / ____ / 20____   ○ ○ ○ ○ ○ ○ ○
                             S M T W TH F S

GETTING STARTED

I am grateful for:

Today's intention (in a word):

MARGIN
MADNESS

Supporting behavior(s):

WRAPPING UP

So, how did your day go? ☹ 😐 🙂 😊

What's your high-five to yourself?

Magical Moments:
(moments/people/experiences)

Intention you'd like to take into sleep with you?

MUSINGS · POPPED UP · REMEMBER · THINK · DOODLE · INNOVATE

Why should I henceforth not love my dreams and not make their riddling images into objects of my daily consideration?

CARL JUNG

DATE ____ / ____ / 20____

○ ○ ○ ○ ○ ○ ○
S M T W TH F S

GETTING STARTED

I am grateful for:

MARGIN
MADNESS

Today's intention (in a word):

Supporting behavior(s):

INNOVATE · DOODLE · THINK · REMEMBER · POPPED UP · MUSINGS

WRAPPING UP

So, how did your day go? ☹ 😐 😊 😄

What's your high-five to yourself?

Magical Moments:
(moments/people/experiences)

Intention you'd like to take into sleep with you?

Everybody is a genuis. But if you judge a fish by its ability to climb a tree, it will live its whole life believing that it is stupid.

ALBERT EINSTEIN

DATE ____ / ____ / 20____

○ ○ ○ ○ ○ ○ ○
S M T W TH F S

GETTING STARTED

I am grateful for:

Today's intention (in a word):

Supporting behavior(s):

WRAPPING UP

So, how did your day go? ☹ 😐 🙂 😊

What's your high-five to yourself?

Magical Moments:
(moments/people/experiences)

Intention you'd like to take into sleep with you?

Continuous improvement is better than delayed perfection.

DATE ____ / ____ / 20___

○ ○ ○ ○ ○ ○ ○
S M T W TH F S

GETTING STARTED

I am grateful for:

MARGIN
MADNESS

Today's intention (in a word):

Supporting behavior(s):

WRAPPING UP

So, how did your day go? ☹ 😐 🙂 😊

What's your high-five to yourself?

Magical Moments:
(moments/people/experiences)

Intention you'd like to take into sleep with you?

MUSINGS · POPPED UP · REMEMBER · THINK · DOODLE · INNOVATE

Never let the future disturb you. You will meet it, if you have to, with the same weapons of reason which today arm you against the present.

MARCUS AURELIUS

DATE ____ / ____ / 20____

○ ○ ○ ○ ○ ○ ○
S M T W TH F S

GETTING STARTED

I am grateful for:

Today's intention (in a word):

Supporting behavior(s):

MARGIN
MADNESS

WRAPPING UP

So, how did your day go? ☹ 😐 🙂 😊

What's your high-five to yourself?

Magical Moments:
(moments/people/experiences)

Intention you'd like to take into sleep with you?

MUSINGS · POPPED UP · REMEMBER · THINK · DOODLE · INNOVATE

You must do the things you think you cannot do.
ELEANOR ROOSEVELT

DATE ____ / ____ / 20____

○ ○ ○ ○ ○ ○ ○
S M T W TH F S

GETTING STARTED

I am grateful for:

MARGIN
MADNESS

Today's intention (in a word):

Supporting behavior(s):

MUSINGS · POPPED UP · REMEMBER · THINK · DOODLE · INNOVATE

WRAPPING UP

So, how did your day go? ☹ 😐 🙂 😊

What's your high-five to yourself?

Magical Moments:
(moments/people/experiences)

Intention you'd like to take into sleep with you?

Gratitude in Action

The indispensable first step to getting the things you want out of life is this: decide what you want.

BEN STEIN

Make a list of some things you want to experience in the next twelve months/three years/five years. Be bold.

ACTION TAKEN:	FEELINGS EXPERIENCED:
THINGS LEARNED/ OBSERVED:	WOULD I DO THIS AGAIN? WHY?

To be yourself in a world that is constantly trying to make you something else is the greatest accomplishment.

RALPH WALDO EMERSON

DATE _____ / _____ / 20_____

○ ○ ○ ○ ○ ○ ○
S M T W TH F S

GETTING STARTED

I am grateful for:

MARGIN
MADNESS

Today's intention (in a word):

Supporting behavior(s):

INNOVATE · DOODLE · THINK · REMEMBER · POPPED UP · MUSINGS

WRAPPING UP

So, how did your day go? ☹ 😐 🙂 😊

What's your high-five to yourself?

Magical Moments:
(moments/people/experiences)

Intention you'd like to take into sleep with you?

Diversity: the art of thinking independently together.

MALCOLM FORBES

DATE ____ / ____ / 20____

O O O O O O O
S M T W TH F S

GETTING STARTED

I am grateful for:

Today's intention (in a word):

MARGIN
MADNESS

Supporting behavior(s):

WRAPPING UP

So, how did your day go? ☹ 😐 😃 😊

What's your high-five to yourself?

Magical Moments:
(moments/people/experiences)

Intention you'd like to take into sleep with you?

MUSINGS · POPPED UP · REMEMBER · THINK · DOODLE · INNOVATE

Find yourself, and be that.
ANON

DATE ____ / ____ / 20____   ○ ○ ○ ○ ○ ○ ○
                             S M T W TH F S

GETTING STARTED

I am grateful for:

MARGIN
MADNESS

Today's intention (in a word):

Supporting behavior(s):

WRAPPING UP

So, how did your day go? ☹ 😐 🙂 😊

What's your high-five to yourself?

Magical Moments:
(moments/people/experiences)

Intention you'd like to take into sleep with you?

INNOVATE · DOODLE · THINK · REMEMBER · POPPED UP · MUSINGS

It's a helluva start, being able to recognize what makes you happy.

LUCILLE BALL

DATE _____ / _____ / 20_____

○ ○ ○ ○ ○ ○ ○
S M T W TH F S

GETTING STARTED

I am grateful for:

Today's intention (in a word):

Supporting behavior(s):

MARGIN
MADNESS

WRAPPING UP

So, how did your day go? ☹ ☺ ☺ ☺

What's your high-five to yourself?

Magical Moments:
(moments/people/experiences)

Intention you'd like to take into sleep with you?

MUSINGS · POPPED UP · REMEMBER · THINK · DOODLE · INNOVATE

HIGH-FIVE!

You're well on your way to 365 days of life-changing-gratitude!

Gratitude offers you the opportunity to look for the silver lining. But, what if you're a realist? Me too—I don't wear rose-colored glasses, *and* I think it's important to thank the thorn bush for offering beautiful roses. Some days, my journal simply says, "Thank you for the day and the hope of tomorrow". My life isn't perfect; I have plenty of "crappy" days. I don't ignore them, and sometimes the silver lining is invisible to me. I have come to learn I wasn't ready for the truth it wanted me to bear witness to. No worries—it will knock again and again until you are.

This is a great place in your new gratitude world to explore the practice of meditation. There are a lot of great apps and teachers, so find one that your soul resonates with. Try it and retry it until the timing is right for you. It wasn't until seven years into my gratitude practice that meditation lined up and stuck for me. Over those years, I committed to try at least once every month. No forcing, no judging, just lots of learning, exploring, and trying.

The act of creating quiet in the mind through meditation, even if only once a month, starts to clear the clutter. Take it for a spin.

Go to the edge of the cliff and jump off. Build your wings on the way down.

RAY BRADBURY

DATE ____ / ____ / 20____

○ ○ ○ ○ ○ ○ ○
S M T W TH F S

GETTING STARTED

I am grateful for:

Today's intention (in a word):

Supporting behavior(s):

MARGIN
MADNESS

WRAPPING UP

So, how did your day go? ☹ 😐 🙂 😊

What's your high-five to yourself?

Magical Moments:
(moments/people/experiences)

Intention you'd like to take into sleep with you?

MUSINGS · POPPED UP · REMEMBER · THINK · DOODLE · INNOVATE

To forgive is to set a prisoner free and discover that the prisoner was you.

LUIS B. SMEDES

DATE _____ / _____ / 20_____

○ ○ ○ ○ ○ ○ ○
S M T W TH F S

GETTING STARTED

I am grateful for:

MARGIN MADNESS

Today's intention (in a word):

Supporting behavior(s):

WRAPPING UP

So, how did your day go? ☹ 😐 🙂 😊

What's your high-five to yourself?

Magical Moments:
(moments/people/experiences)

Intention you'd like to take into sleep with you?

INNOVATE · DOODLE · THINK · REMEMBER · POPPED UP · MUSINGS

Moments of reflection splashed with gratitude enable
love to flow and the heart's gates to open.

ALEXSYS THOMPSON

DATE ____ / ____ / 20____

○ ○ ○ ○ ○ ○ ○
S M T W TH F S

GETTING STARTED

I am grateful for:

Today's intention (in a word):

MARGIN
MADNESS

Supporting behavior(s):

WRAPPING UP

So, how did your day go? ☹ 😐 🙂 😊

What's your high-five to yourself?

Magical Moments:
(moments/people/experiences)

Intention you'd like to take into sleep with you?

MUSINGS · POPPED UP · REMEMBER · THINK · DOODLE · INNOVATE

Gratitude in Action

Nobody can't be uncheered with a balloon.
WINNIE THE POOH

**Send someone a balloon.
I double-dog dare you!**

ACTION TAKEN:	FEELINGS EXPERIENCED:
THINGS LEARNED/ OBSERVED:	**WOULD I DO THIS AGAIN? WHY?**

The future belongs to those who believe in the beauty of their dreams.

ELEANOR ROOSEVELT

DATE ____ / ____ / 20____   ○ ○ ○ ○ ○ ○ ○
                              S M T W TH F S

GETTING STARTED

I am grateful for:

Today's intention (in a word):

Supporting behavior(s):

MARGIN
MADNESS

WRAPPING UP

So, how did your day go? ☹ 😐 🙂 😊

What's your high-five to yourself?

Magical Moments:
(moments/people/experiences)

Intention you'd like to take into sleep with you?

MUSINGS · POPPED UP · REMEMBER · THINK · DOODLE · INNOVATE

Ever wonder how many angels you have? All of them.
They insisted.

MIKE DOOLEY

DATE ____ / ____ / 20____

○ ○ ○ ○ ○ ○ ○
S M T W TH F S

GETTING STARTED

I am grateful for:

MARGIN
MADNESS

Today's intention (in a word):

Supporting behavior(s):

INNOVATE · DOODLE · THINK · REMEMBER · POPPED UP · MUSINGS

WRAPPING UP

So, how did your day go? ☹ 😐 🙂 😊

What's your high-five to yourself?

Magical Moments:
(moments/people/experiences)

Intention you'd like to take into sleep with you?

Happiness is a state of activity.
CONFUCIUS

DATE ____ / ____ / 20____   ○ ○ ○ ○ ○ ○ ○
                             S M T W TH F S

GETTING STARTED

I am grateful for:

Today's intention (in a word):

MARGIN
MADNESS

Supporting behavior(s):

WRAPPING UP

So, how did your day go? ☹ 😐 🙂 😊

What's your high-five to yourself?

Magical Moments:
(moments/people/experiences)

Intention you'd like to take into sleep with you?

MUSINGS · POPPED UP · REMEMBER · THINK · DOODLE · INNOVATE

Egotism is the source and summary of all faults and miseries.

THOMAS CARLYLE

DATE _____ / _____ / 20_____   ○ ○ ○ ○ ○ ○ ○
                                       S M T W TH F S

GETTING STARTED

I am grateful for:

MARGIN
MADNESS

Today's intention (in a word):

Supporting behavior(s):

WRAPPING UP

So, how did your day go? ☹ 😐 😃 😊

What's your high-five to yourself?

Magical Moments:
(moments/people/experiences)

Intention you'd like to take into sleep with you?

MUSINGS · POPPED UP · REMEMBER · THINK · DOODLE · INNOVATE

We are all of us stars, and we deserve to twinkle.
MARILYN MONROE

DATE ____ / ____ / 20____   ○ ○ ○ ○ ○ ○ ○
                             S M T W TH F S

GETTING STARTED

I am grateful for:

Today's intention (in a word):

Supporting behavior(s):

MARGIN
MADNESS

WRAPPING UP

So, how did your day go? ☹ 😐 🙂 😊

What's your high-five to yourself?

Magical Moments:
(moments/people/experiences)

Intention you'd like to take into sleep with you?

MUSINGS · POPPED UP · REMEMBER · THINK · DOODLE · INNOVATE

There are always flowers for those who want to see them.

HENRI MATISSE

DATE ____ / ____ / 20____

○ ○ ○ ○ ○ ○ ○
S M T W TH F S

GETTING STARTED

I am grateful for:

MARGIN
MADNESS

Today's intention (in a word):

Supporting behavior(s):

INNOVATE · DOODLE · THINK · REMEMBER · POPPED UP · MUSINGS

WRAPPING UP

So, how did your day go? ☹ 😐 🙂 😊

What's your high-five to yourself?

Magical Moments:
(moments/people/experiences)

Intention you'd like to take into sleep with you?

Listen! The wind is rising, and the air is wild with leaves,
We have had our summer evenings, now for October eves!

DATE _____ / _____ / 20_____

○ ○ ○ ○ ○ ○ ○
S M T W TH F S

GETTING STARTED

I am grateful for:

Today's intention (in a word):

Supporting behavior(s):

WRAPPING UP

So, how did your day go? ☹ 😐 😊 🙂

What's your high-five to yourself?

Magical Moments:
(moments/people/experiences)

Intention you'd like to take into sleep with you?

MUSINGS · POPPED UP · REMEMBER · THINK · DOODLE · INNOVATE

If we have no peace, it is because we have forgotten that we belong to each other.

MOTHER THERESA

DATE ____ / ____ / 20____

○ ○ ○ ○ ○ ○ ○
S M T W TH F S

GETTING STARTED

I am grateful for:

MARGIN MADNESS

Today's intention (in a word):

Supporting behavior(s):

WRAPPING UP

So, how did your day go? ☹ 😐 🙂 😊

What's your high-five to yourself?

Magical Moments:
(moments/people/experiences)

Intention you'd like to take into sleep with you?

INNOVATE · DOODLE · THINK · REMEMBER · POPPED UP · MUSINGS

Gratitude in Action

If you are too busy to laugh, you are too busy.
PROVERB

Find someone to share a laugh with; relish in it.

ACTION TAKEN:	FEELINGS EXPERIENCED:
THINGS LEARNED/ OBSERVED:	**WOULD I DO THIS AGAIN? WHY?**

Pride must die in you, or nothing of heaven can live in you.
ANDREW MURRAY

DATE ____ / ____ / 20____   O O O O O O O
                                  S M T W TH F S

GETTING STARTED

I am grateful for:

MARGIN
MADNESS

Today's intention (in a word):

Supporting behavior(s):

WRAPPING UP

So, how did your day go? ☹ 😐 🙂 😊
What's your high-five to yourself?

Magical Moments:
(moments/people/experiences)

Intention you'd like to take into sleep with you?

INNOVATE · DOODLE · THINK · REMEMBER · POPPED UP · MUSINGS

Thanks for noticin' me.
EEYORE

DATE ____ / ____ / 20____

○ ○ ○ ○ ○ ○ ○
S M T W TH F S

GETTING STARTED

I am grateful for:

Today's intention (in a word):

Supporting behavior(s):

MARGIN
MADNESS

WRAPPING UP

So, how did your day go? ☹ 😐 🙂 😊

What's your high-five to yourself?

Magical Moments:
(moments/people/experiences)

Intention you'd like to take into sleep with you?

MUSINGS · POPPED UP · REMEMBER · THINK · DOODLE · INNOVATE

I have never been remotely ashamed of having been depressed. Never. What's to be ashamed of? I went through a really rough time and I am quite proud that I got out of that.

JK ROWLING

DATE _____ / _____ / 20_____

○ ○ ○ ○ ○ ○ ○
S M T W TH F S

GETTING STARTED

I am grateful for:

Today's intention (in a word):

Supporting behavior(s):

WRAPPING UP

So, how did your day go? ☹ 😐 🙂 😊

What's your high-five to yourself?

Magical Moments:
(moments/people/experiences)

Intention you'd like to take into sleep with you?

I believe in destiny. There must be a reason that I am as I am. There must be.

ROBIN WILLIAMS

DATE ____ / ____ / 20____

○ ○ ○ ○ ○ ○ ○
S M T W TH F S

GETTING STARTED

I am grateful for:

Today's intention (in a word):

Supporting behavior(s):

MARGIN
MADNESS

WRAPPING UP

So, how did your day go? ☹ 😕 🙂 😊

What's your high-five to yourself?

Magical Moments:
(moments/people/experiences)

Intention you'd like to take into sleep with you?

MUSINGS · POPPED UP · REMEMBER · THINK · DOODLE · INNOVATE

You are imperfect, you are wired for struggle, but you are worthy of love and belonging.

BRENÉ BROWN

DATE ____ / ____ / 20____

○ ○ ○ ○ ○ ○ ○
S M T W TH F S

GETTING STARTED

I am grateful for:

MARGIN
MADNESS

Today's intention (in a word):

Supporting behavior(s):

WRAPPING UP

So, how did your day go? ☹ ☹ ☺ ☺

What's your high-five to yourself?

Magical Moments:
(moments/people/experiences)

Intention you'd like to take into sleep with you?

MUSINGS · POPPED UP · REMEMBER · THINK · DOODLE · INNOVATE

If you aren't over your head, how do you know how tall you are?

T.S. ELIOT

DATE ____ / ____ / 20____   ○ ○ ○ ○ ○ ○ ○
                              S M T W TH F S

GETTING STARTED

I am grateful for:

Today's intention (in a word):

Supporting behavior(s):

MARGIN
MADNESS

WRAPPING UP

So, how did your day go?   ☹ 😐 😀 ☺

What's your high-five to yourself?

Magical Moments:
(moments/people/experiences)

Intention you'd like to take into sleep with you?

MUSINGS · POPPED UP · REMEMBER · THINK · DOODLE · INNOVATE

Gratitude in Action

We don't stop playing because we grow old; we grow old because we stop playing.

GEORGE BERNARD SHAW

Play a game with someone.

ACTION TAKEN:	FEELINGS EXPERIENCED:
THINGS LEARNED/ OBSERVED:	WOULD I DO THIS AGAIN? WHY?

Nothing great was ever achieved without enthusiam.
RALPH WALDO EMERSON

DATE ____ / ____ / 20___

○ ○ ○ ○ ○ ○ ○
S M T W TH F S

GETTING STARTED

I am grateful for:

Today's intention (in a word):

MARGIN
MADNESS

Supporting behavior(s):

WRAPPING UP

So, how did your day go? ☹ 😐 😊 😊

What's your high-five to yourself?

Magical Moments:
(moments/people/experiences)

Intention you'd like to take into sleep with you?

MUSINGS · POPPED UP · REMEMBER · THINK · DOODLE · INNOVATE

Every great dream begins with a dreamer. Always remember, you have within you the strength, the patience, and the passion to reach for the stars to change the world.

HARRIET TUBMAN

DATE ____ / ____ / 20____

○ ○ ○ ○ ○ ○ ○
S M T W TH F S

GETTING STARTED

I am grateful for:

MARGIN
MADNESS

Today's intention (in a word):

Supporting behavior(s):

INNOVATE · DOODLE · THINK · REMEMBER · POPPED UP · MUSINGS

WRAPPING UP

So, how did your day go? ☹ 😐 🙂 😊

What's your high-five to yourself?

Magical Moments:
(moments/people/experiences)

Intention you'd like to take into sleep with you?

Forgiveness is one of the greatest acts of self-love you can do for yourself.

ALEXSYS THOMPSON

DATE ____ / ____ / 20____

○ ○ ○ ○ ○ ○ ○
S M T W TH F S

GETTING STARTED

I am grateful for:

Today's intention (in a word):

MARGIN
MADNESS

Supporting behavior(s):

WRAPPING UP

So, how did your day go? ☹ 😐 🙂 😊

What's your high-five to yourself?

Magical Moments:
(moments/people/experiences)

Intention you'd like to take into sleep with you?

MUSINGS · POPPED UP · REMEMBER · THINK · DOODLE · INNOVATE

Stop acting so small. You are the Universe in ecstatic motion.

RUMI

DATE _____ / _____ / 20_____   ○ ○ ○ ○ ○ ○ ○
                                  S M T W TH F S

GETTING STARTED

I am grateful for:

MARGIN
MADNESS

Today's intention (in a word):

Supporting behavior(s):

WRAPPING UP

So, how did your day go? ☹ 😐 🙂 😊

What's your high-five to yourself?

Magical Moments:
(moments/people/experiences)

Intention you'd like to take into sleep with you?

MUSINGS · POPPED UP · REMEMBER · THINK · DOODLE · INNOVATE

Don't talk about yourself; it will be done when you leave.
WILSON MIZNER

DATE ____ / ____ / 20____

○ ○ ○ ○ ○ ○ ○
S M T W TH F S

GETTING STARTED

I am grateful for:

Today's intention (in a word):

Supporting behavior(s):

MARGIN
MADNESS

WRAPPING UP

So, how did your day go? ☹ 😐 🙂 😊

What's your high-five to yourself?

Magical Moments:
(moments/people/experiences)

Intention you'd like to take into sleep with you?

MUSINGS · POPPED UP · REMEMBER · THINK · DOODLE · INNOVATE

> *Nature always wears the colors of the spirit.*
> RALPH WALDO EMERSON

DATE ____ / ____ / 20____   ○ ○ ○ ○ ○ ○ ○
                                 S M T W TH F S

GETTING STARTED

I am grateful for:

MARGIN
MADNESS

Today's intention (in a word):

Supporting behavior(s):

INNOVATE · DOODLE · THINK · REMEMBER · POPPED UP · MUSINGS

WRAPPING UP

So, how did your day go? ☹ 😐 🙂 😊

What's your high-five to yourself?

Magical Moments:
(moments/people/experiences)

Intention you'd like to take into sleep with you?

People stuck in the past are doomed to repeat it. People who fear for the future are bound to meet it. Those who live in the moment are sure to enjoy it.

AUTHOR UNKNOWN

DATE _____ / _____ / 20_____

○ ○ ○ ○ ○ ○ ○
S M T W TH F S

GETTING STARTED

I am grateful for:

Today's intention (in a word):

Supporting behavior(s):

MARGIN
MADNESS

WRAPPING UP

So, how did your day go? ☹ 😐 😊 ☺

What's your high-five to yourself?

Magical Moments:
(moments/people/experiences)

Intention you'd like to take into sleep with you?

MUSINGS · POPPED UP · REMEMBER · THINK · DOODLE · INNOVATE

*I don't think anyone, until their soul leaves their body, is
past the point of no return.*
TOM HIDDLESTON

DATE ____ / ____ / 20____

○ ○ ○ ○ ○ ○ ○
S M T W TH F S

GETTING STARTED

I am grateful for:

MARGIN
MADNESS

Today's intention (in a word):

Supporting behavior(s):

WRAPPING UP

So, how did your day go? ☹ 😐 🙂 😊

What's your high-five to yourself?

Magical Moments:
(moments/people/experiences)

Intention you'd like to take into sleep with you?

INNOVATE · DOODLE · THINK · REMEMBER · POPPED UP · MUSINGS

What lies behind you and what lies in front of you pales in comparison to what lies inside you.

RALPH WALDO EMERSON

DATE ____ / ____ / 20____

○ ○ ○ ○ ○ ○ ○
S M T W TH F S

GETTING STARTED

I am grateful for:

Today's intention (in a word):

Supporting behavior(s):

MARGIN MADNESS

WRAPPING UP

So, how did your day go? ☹ ☹ ☺ ☺

What's your high-five to yourself?

Magical Moments:
(moments/people/experiences)

Intention you'd like to take into sleep with you?

MUSINGS · POPPED UP · REMEMBER · THINK · DOODLE · INNOVATE

Among those whom I like or admire, I can find no common denominator, but among those whom I love, I can; all of them make me laugh.

W.H. AUDEN

DATE ____ / ____ / 20____

○ ○ ○ ○ ○ ○ ○
S M T W TH F S

GETTING STARTED

I am grateful for:

MARGIN
MADNESS

Today's intention (in a word):

Supporting behavior(s):

WRAPPING UP

So, how did your day go? ☹ 😐 🙂 😊

What's your high-five to yourself?

Magical Moments:
(moments/people/experiences)

Intention you'd like to take into sleep with you?

MUSINGS · POPPED UP · REMEMBER · THINK · DOODLE · INNOVATE

Gratitude in Action

Most people are about as happy as they make up their minds to be.

ABRAHAM LINCOLN

Ask three people what makes them happy. Share what makes you happy.

ACTION TAKEN:	FEELINGS EXPERIENCED:
THINGS LEARNED/ OBSERVED:	WOULD I DO THIS AGAIN? WHY?

*You will have bad times, but they will always wake you
up to the stuff you weren't paying attention to.*
ROBIN WILLIAMS

DATE ____ / ____ / 20____

○ ○ ○ ○ ○ ○ ○
S M T W TH F S

GETTING STARTED

I am grateful for:

MARGIN
MADNESS

Today's intention (in a word):

Supporting behavior(s):

INNOVATE · DOODLE · THINK · REMEMBER · POPPED UP · MUSINGS

WRAPPING UP

So, how did your day go? ☹ 😐 🙂 😊

What's your high-five to yourself?

Magical Moments:
(moments/people/experiences)

Intention you'd like to take into sleep with you?

I love people who make me laugh. I honestly think it's the thing I like most, to laugh. It cures a multitude of ills. It's probably the most important thing in a person.

AUDREY HEPBURN

DATE ____ / ____ / 20___

○ ○ ○ ○ ○ ○ ○
S M T W TH F S

GETTING STARTED

I am grateful for:

Today's intention (in a word):

MARGIN
MADNESS

Supporting behavior(s):

WRAPPING UP

So, how did your day go? ☹ 😐 😊 😃

What's your high-five to yourself?

Magical Moments:
(moments/people/experiences)

Intention you'd like to take into sleep with you?

MUSINGS · POPPED UP · REMEMBER · THINK · DOODLE · INNOVATE

When the power of love overcomes the love of power,
the world will know peace.

JIMMY HENDRIX

DATE ____ / ____ / 20____

○ ○ ○ ○ ○ ○ ○
S M T W TH F S

GETTING STARTED

I am grateful for:

MARGIN
MADNESS

Today's intention (in a word):

Supporting behavior(s):

WRAPPING UP

So, how did your day go? ☹ 😕 🙂 ☺
What's your high-five to yourself?

Magical Moments:
(moments/people/experiences)

Intention you'd like to take into sleep with you?

INNOVATE · DOODLE · THINK · REMEMBER · POPPED UP · MUSINGS

How lucky I am to have something that makes saying goodbye so hard.

WINNIE THE POOH

DATE ____ / ____ / 20____

○ ○ ○ ○ ○ ○ ○
S M T W TH F S

GETTING STARTED

I am grateful for:

Today's intention (in a word):

MARGIN
MADNESS

Supporting behavior(s):

WRAPPING UP

So, how did your day go? ☹ 😐 😊 😃

What's your high-five to yourself?

Magical Moments:
(moments/people/experiences)

Intention you'd like to take into sleep with you?

MUSINGS • POPPED UP • REMEMBER • THINK • DOODLE • INNOVATE

No one can make you feel inferior without your consent.

ELEANOR ROOSEVELT

DATE ____ / ____ / 20____

GETTING STARTED

I am grateful for:

MARGIN
MADNESS

Today's intention (in a word):

Supporting behavior(s):

WRAPPING UP

So, how did your day go? ☹ 😐 🙂 😊

What's your high-five to yourself?

Magical Moments:
(moments/people/experiences)

Intention you'd like to take into sleep with you?

MUSINGS · POPPED UP · REMEMBER · THINK · DOODLE · INNOVATE

A lot of different flowers make a bouquet.

MUSLIM PROVERB

DATE _____ / _____ / 20_____

○ ○ ○ ○ ○ ○ ○
S M T W TH F S

GETTING STARTED

I am grateful for:

Today's intention (in a word):

Supporting behavior(s):

MARGIN
MADNESS

WRAPPING UP

So, how did your day go? ☹ 😐 😊 😃

What's your high-five to yourself?

Magical Moments:
(moments/people/experiences)

Intention you'd like to take into sleep with you?

MUSINGS · POPPED UP · REMEMBER · THINK · DOODLE · INNOVATE

Gratitude in Action

Sure is a cheerful color. Guess I'll have to get used to it.
EEYORE

Find something colorful and share it to brighten someone's day.

ACTION TAKEN:	FEELINGS EXPERIENCED:
THINGS LEARNED/ OBSERVED:	**WOULD I DO THIS AGAIN? WHY?**

The human soul needs actual beauty more than bread.

D.H. LAWRENCE

DATE ____ / ____ / 20____

○ ○ ○ ○ ○ ○ ○
S M T W TH F S

GETTING STARTED

I am grateful for:

Today's intention (in a word):

MARGIN
MADNESS

Supporting behavior(s):

WRAPPING UP

So, how did your day go? ☹ ☺ ☺ ☺

What's your high-five to yourself?

Magical Moments:
(moments/people/experiences)

Intention you'd like to take into sleep with you?

MUSINGS · POPPED UP · REMEMBER · THINK · DOODLE · INNOVATE

The greatest human desire is to be seen, heard, and understood.

ALEXSYS THOMPSON

DATE ____ / ____ / 20____   ○ ○ ○ ○ ○ ○ ○
                              S M T W TH F S

GETTING STARTED

I am grateful for:

MARGIN
MADNESS

Today's intention (in a word):

Supporting behavior(s):

WRAPPING UP

So, how did your day go? ☹ ☺ ☺ ☺

What's your high-five to yourself?

Magical Moments:
(moments/people/experiences)

Intention you'd like to take into sleep with you?

MUSINGS · POPPED UP · REMEMBER · THINK · DOODLE · INNOVATE

No matter what people tell you, words and ideas can change the world.

ROBIN WILLIAMS

DATE ____ / ____ / 20____

○ ○ ○ ○ ○ ○ ○
S M T W TH F S

GETTING STARTED

I am grateful for:

Today's intention (in a word):

Supporting behavior(s):

MARGIN
MADNESS

WRAPPING UP

So, how did your day go? ☹ 😐 🙂 😊

What's your high-five to yourself?

Magical Moments:
(moments/people/experiences)

Intention you'd like to take into sleep with you?

MUSINGS · POPPED UP · REMEMBER · THINK · DOODLE · INNOVATE

The truth is, no one of us is free until everybody is free.

MAYA ANGELOU

DATE ____ / ____ / 20___   ○ ○ ○ ○ ○ ○ ○
                              S M T W TH F S

GETTING STARTED

I am grateful for:

MARGIN
MADNESS

Today's intention (in a word):

Supporting behavior(s):

MUSINGS · POPPED UP · REMEMBER · THINK · DOODLE · INNOVATE

WRAPPING UP

So, how did your day go?   ☹ 😐 🙂 😊

What's your high-five to yourself?

Magical Moments:
(moments/people/experiences)

Intention you'd like to take into sleep with you?

TIME IS A GIFT

I would like to share some of my hopes for you at this point in your journey:

- I hope you have taken on a "Gratitude in Action" at least once a month and that you are realizing gratitude *in action* is like a magnet for finding your flow

- I hope you have shared your practice with a few people aloud and perhaps even sent them a journal (smiles)

- I hope your curiosity is heightened in all you do and judgment is suspended

- I hope you are eager to share your high-fives with yourself and let them enter every fiber of your body

- I hope you have uncovered some long-lost joys in the margins and white space of your journal

- I hope the force to keep on going all the way with this practice is with you

So powerful is the light of unity that it can illuminate the whole earth.

BAHA WRITING

DATE ____ / ____ / 20____

○ ○ ○ ○ ○ ○ ○
S M T W TH F S

GETTING STARTED

I am grateful for:

MARGIN
MADNESS

Today's intention (in a word):

Supporting behavior(s):

WRAPPING UP

So, how did your day go? ☹ ☹ ☺ ☺

What's your high-five to yourself?

Magical Moments:
(moments/people/experiences)

Intention you'd like to take into sleep with you?

INNOVATE · DOODLE · THINK · REMEMBER · POPPED UP · MUSINGS

Everything feels absolutely new and so familiar at the same time.

ALEXSYS THOMPSON

DATE ____ / ____ / 20____

○ ○ ○ ○ ○ ○ ○
S M T W TH F S

GETTING STARTED

I am grateful for:

Today's intention (in a word):

MARGIN
MADNESS

Supporting behavior(s):

WRAPPING UP

So, how did your day go? ☹ 😐 🙂 😊

What's your high-five to yourself?

Magical Moments:
(moments/people/experiences)

Intention you'd like to take into sleep with you?

MUSINGS · POPPED UP · REMEMBER · THINK · DOODLE · INNOVATE

The only thing worse than starting something and failing ... is not starting something.

SETH GODIN

DATE ____ / ____ / 20___

○ ○ ○ ○ ○ ○ ○
S M T W TH F S

GETTING STARTED

I am grateful for:

MARGIN MADNESS

Today's intention (in a word):

Supporting behavior(s):

WRAPPING UP

So, how did your day go? ☹ 😐 🙂 😊

What's your high-five to yourself?

Magical Moments:
(moments/people/experiences)

Intention you'd like to take into sleep with you?

MUSINGS · POPPED UP · REMEMBER · THINK · DOODLE · INNOVATE

Gratitude in Action

My spelling is Wobbly. It's good spelling but it Wobbles, and the letters get in the wrong places.

WINNIE THE POOH

Write a letter to someone and mail it today. Let it wobble—perfection is not the goal. Oh, and put your computer away; try pen and paper.

ACTION TAKEN:	FEELINGS EXPERIENCED:
THINGS LEARNED/ OBSERVED:	**WOULD I DO THIS AGAIN? WHY?**

Spring is the time of year when it is summer in the sun and winter in the shade.

CHARLES DICKENS

DATE ____ / ____ / 20____

O O O O O O O
S M T W TH F S

GETTING STARTED

I am grateful for:

Today's intention (in a word):

Supporting behavior(s):

WRAPPING UP

So, how did your day go? ☹ 😐 🙂 😊

What's your high-five to yourself?

Magical Moments:
(moments/people/experiences)

Intention you'd like to take into sleep with you?

Flowers... are a proud assertion that a ray of beauty outvalues all the utilities of the world.

AUTHOR UNKNOWN

DATE ____ / ____ / 20____   O O O O O O O
                                   S M T W TH F S

GETTING STARTED

I am grateful for:

Today's intention (in a word):

Supporting behavior(s):

MARGIN
MADNESS

WRAPPING UP

So, how did your day go? ☹ 😐 😃 😊

What's your high-five to yourself?

Magical Moments:
(moments/people/experiences)

Intention you'd like to take into sleep with you?

MUSINGS · POPPED UP · REMEMBER · THINK · DOODLE · INNOVATE

If failure is the way to success, then try is the path there.

ALEXSYS THOMPSON

DATE _____ / _____ / 20_____   ○ ○ ○ ○ ○ ○ ○
                                 S M T W TH F S

GETTING STARTED

I am grateful for:

MARGIN
MADNESS

Today's intention (in a word):

Supporting behavior(s):

WRAPPING UP

So, how did your day go? 😦 😐 😊 ☺

What's your high-five to yourself?

Magical Moments:
(moments/people/experiences)

Intention you'd like to take into sleep with you?

MUSINGS · POPPED UP · REMEMBER · THINK · DOODLE · INNOVATE

No act of kindness, no matter how small, is ever wasted.
AESOP

DATE ____ / ____ / 20____

○ ○ ○ ○ ○ ○ ○
S M T W TH F S

GETTING STARTED

I am grateful for:

Today's intention (in a word):

Supporting behavior(s):

MARGIN
MADNESS

WRAPPING UP

So, how did your day go? ☹ 😐 🙂 😊

What's your high-five to yourself?

Magical Moments:
(moments/people/experiences)

Intention you'd like to take into sleep with you?

MUSINGS · POPPED UP · REMEMBER · THINK · DOODLE · INNOVATE

Always the more beautiful answer who asks the more beautiful question.

E.E. CUMMINGS

DATE ____ / ____ / 20____

○ ○ ○ ○ ○ ○ ○
S M T W TH F S

GETTING STARTED

I am grateful for:

MARGIN
MADNESS

Today's intention (in a word):

Supporting behavior(s):

INNOVATE · DOODLE · THINK · REMEMBER · POPPED UP · MUSINGS

WRAPPING UP

So, how did your day go? ☹ 😐 🙂 😊

What's your high-five to yourself?

Magical Moments:
(moments/people/experiences)

Intention you'd like to take into sleep with you?

Music is an outburst of the soul.

FREDERICK DELIUS

DATE ____ / ____ / 20____

○ ○ ○ ○ ○ ○ ○
S M T W TH F S

GETTING STARTED

I am grateful for:

Today's intention (in a word):

MARGIN
MADNESS

Supporting behavior(s):

WRAPPING UP

So, how did your day go? ☹ 😐 😊 😄

What's your high-five to yourself?

Magical Moments:
(moments/people/experiences)

Intention you'd like to take into sleep with you?

MUSINGS • POPPED UP • REMEMBER • THINK • DOODLE • INNOVATE

Gratitude in Action

Say not, in grief that she has gone, but give thanks that she was yours.

AUTHOR UNKNOWN

Look back and offer thanks for the blessings someone brought into your life despite them not being around any longer. Share this with a friend, out loud.

ACTION TAKEN:	FEELINGS EXPERIENCED:
THINGS LEARNED/ OBSERVED:	**WOULD I DO THIS AGAIN? WHY?**

Life will bring you pain all by itself. Your responsibility is to create joy.

MILTON ERICKSON

DATE ____ / ____ / 20____

O O O O O O O
S M T W TH F S

GETTING STARTED

I am grateful for:

Today's intention (in a word):

MARGIN
MADNESS

Supporting behavior(s):

WRAPPING UP

So, how did your day go? ☹ 😐 🙂 😊

What's your high-five to yourself?

Magical Moments:
(moments/people/experiences)

Intention you'd like to take into sleep with you?

MUSINGS · POPPED UP · REMEMBER · THINK · DOODLE · INNOVATE

When I had nothing to lose, I had everything. When I stopped being who I am, I found myself.

PAULO COELHO

DATE ____ / ____ / 20____   ○ ○ ○ ○ ○ ○ ○
                              S M T W TH F S

GETTING STARTED

I am grateful for:

MARGIN
MADNESS

Today's intention (in a word):

Supporting behavior(s):

WRAPPING UP

So, how did your day go? ☹ 😐 🙂 😊

What's your high-five to yourself?

Magical Moments:
(moments/people/experiences)

Intention you'd like to take into sleep with you?

MUSINGS · POPPED UP · REMEMBER · THINK · DOODLE · INNOVATE

You are a beautiful soul hidden by the trench coat of the ego.

MIKE DOLAN

DATE ____ / ____ / 20____   ○ ○ ○ ○ ○ ○ ○
                                S M T W TH F S

GETTING STARTED

I am grateful for:

Today's intention (in a word):

MARGIN
MADNESS

Supporting behavior(s):

WRAPPING UP

So, how did your day go? ☹ 😐 🙂 😊

What's your high-five to yourself?

Magical Moments:
(moments/people/experiences)

Intention you'd like to take into sleep with you?

MUSINGS · POPPED UP · REMEMBER · THINK · DOODLE · INNOVATE

"Thank you" is the best prayer that anyone could say. I say that one a lot. Thank you expresses extreme gratitude, humility, understanding.

ALICE WALKER

DATE ____ / ____ / 20____

○ ○ ○ ○ ○ ○ ○
S M T W TH F S

GETTING STARTED

I am grateful for:

MARGIN
MADNESS

Today's intention (in a word):

Supporting behavior(s):

INNOVATE · DOODLE · THINK · REMEMBER · POPPED UP · MUSINGS

WRAPPING UP

So, how did your day go? ☹ 😐 🙂 😊

What's your high-five to yourself?

Magical Moments:
(moments/people/experiences)

Intention you'd like to take into sleep with you?

*Although gold dust is precious, when it gets in your eyes
it obstructs your vision.*

HIS-TANG CHIH TSANG

DATE ____ / ____ / 20____

○ ○ ○ ○ ○ ○ ○
S M T W TH F S

GETTING STARTED

I am grateful for:

MARGIN
MADNESS

Today's intention (in a word):

Supporting behavior(s):

WRAPPING UP

So, how did your day go? ☹ 😕 😐 ☺

What's your high-five to yourself?

Magical Moments:
(moments/people/experiences)

Intention you'd like to take into sleep with you?

MUSINGS · POPPED UP · REMEMBER · THINK · DOODLE · INNOVATE

It (Life) is constantly changing, and yet it remains the same.

JAN HAWKINS

DATE ____ / ____ / 20____

○ ○ ○ ○ ○ ○ ○
S M T W TH F S

GETTING STARTED

I am grateful for:

MARGIN
MADNESS

Today's intention (in a word):

Supporting behavior(s):

WRAPPING UP

So, how did your day go? ☹ 😐 🙂 😊

What's your high-five to yourself?

Magical Moments:
(moments/people/experiences)

Intention you'd like to take into sleep with you?

MUSINGS · POPPED UP · REMEMBER · THINK · DOODLE · INNOVATE

I thank God for this most amazing day, for the leafing greenly spirits of trees and for the blue sky and for the everything which is natural, which is infinite, which is yes.

E.E. CUMMINGS

DATE ____ / ____ / 20____

○ ○ ○ ○ ○ ○ ○
S M T W TH F S

GETTING STARTED

I am grateful for:

Today's intention (in a word):

Supporting behavior(s):

MARGIN
MADNESS

WRAPPING UP

So, how did your day go? ☹ 😐 😊 ☺

What's your high-five to yourself?

Magical Moments:
(moments/people/experiences)

Intention you'd like to take into sleep with you?

MUSINGS · POPPED UP · REMEMBER · THINK · DOODLE · INNOVATE

It is not your outward appearance that you should beautify, but your soul, adorning it with good works.

CLEMENT OF ALEXANDRIA

DATE ____ / ____ / 20____

O O O O O O O
S M T W TH F S

GETTING STARTED

I am grateful for:

MARGIN MADNESS

Today's intention (in a word):

Supporting behavior(s):

MUSINGS · POPPED UP · REMEMBER · THINK · DOODLE · INNOVATE

WRAPPING UP

So, how did your day go? ☹ 😐 🙂 😊

What's your high-five to yourself?

Magical Moments:
(moments/people/experiences)

Intention you'd like to take into sleep with you?

Gratitude in Action

Food-sharing is an innate way that we show our love for people we care about. Including others in times of celebration is an act of kindness.

DR. THERESA NICASSIO

Share a meal with someone you've been meaning to reconnect with.

ACTION TAKEN:	FEELINGS EXPERIENCED:
THINGS LEARNED/ OBSERVED:	WOULD I DO THIS AGAIN? WHY?

ALMOST THERE

Congratulations on almost completing half-a-year or so of choosing gratitude!

You will never again see the world through the same lens. The sense of curiosity you have developed has most likely shifted many things in your life. Take a moment and jot down some of the shifts you have experienced through the process. Remember this is your journal—no right or wrong answers, just YOUR answers. Try not to edit yourself, let it flow.

Enlightenment is ego's ultimate disappointment.

CHOGYANN TRUNGPA

DATE ____ / ____ / 20____   O O O O O O O
                                    S M T W TH F S

GETTING STARTED

I am grateful for:

Today's intention (in a word):

MARGIN
MADNESS

Supporting behavior(s):

WRAPPING UP

So, how did your day go? ☹ 😐 🙂 😊

What's your high-five to yourself?

Magical Moments:
(moments/people/experiences)

Intention you'd like to take into sleep with you?

MUSINGS · POPPED UP · REMEMBER · THINK · DOODLE · INNOVATE

I can see myself in all things and all people around me.
SANSKRIT SAYING

DATE _____ / _____ / 20_____

○ ○ ○ ○ ○ ○ ○
S M T W TH F S

GETTING STARTED

I am grateful for:

MARGIN
MADNESS

Today's intention (in a word):

Supporting behavior(s):

WRAPPING UP

So, how did your day go? ☹ 😐 🙂 😊

What's your high-five to yourself?

Magical Moments:
(moments/people/experiences)

Intention you'd like to take into sleep with you?

MUSINGS · POPPED UP · REMEMBER · THINK · DOODLE · INNOVATE

God enters by private door into every individual.

RALPH WALDO EMERSON

DATE ____ / ____ / 20____

○ ○ ○ ○ ○ ○ ○
S M T W TH F S

GETTING STARTED

I am grateful for:

Today's intention (in a word):

MARGIN
MADNESS

Supporting behavior(s):

WRAPPING UP

So, how did your day go? ☹ 😕 🙂 😊

What's your high-five to yourself?

Magical Moments:
(moments/people/experiences)

Intention you'd like to take into sleep with you?

MUSINGS · POPPED UP · REMEMBER · THINK · DOODLE · INNOVATE

Everybody needs beauty as well as bread, place to play and pray in, where nature may heal and give strength to body and soul.

JOHN MUIR

DATE ____ / ____ / 20____

○ ○ ○ ○ ○ ○ ○
S M T W TH F S

GETTING STARTED

I am grateful for:

MARGIN
MADNESS

Today's intention (in a word):

Supporting behavior(s):

INNOVATE · DOODLE · THINK · REMEMBER · POPPED UP · MUSINGS

WRAPPING UP

So, how did your day go? ☹ 😐 🙂 😊

What's your high-five to yourself?

Magical Moments:
(moments/people/experiences)

Intention you'd like to take into sleep with you?

If we had no winter, the spring would not be so pleasant: if we did not sometimes taste of adversity, prosperity would not be so welcome.

ANNA BRADSTREET

DATE _____ / _____ / 20_____

○ ○ ○ ○ ○ ○ ○
S M T W TH F S

GETTING STARTED

I am grateful for:

Today's intention (in a word):

Supporting behavior(s):

MARGIN MADNESS

WRAPPING UP

So, how did your day go? ☹ 😐 😀 ☺

What's your high-five to yourself?

Magical Moments:
(moments/people/experiences)

Intention you'd like to take into sleep with you?

MUSINGS · POPPED UP · REMEMBER · THINK · DOODLE · INNOVATE

Forgiveness is me giving up the right to hurt you for hurting me.

AUTHOR UNKNOWN

DATE ____ / ____ / 20____

○ ○ ○ ○ ○ ○ ○
S M T W TH F S

GETTING STARTED

I am grateful for:

Today's intention (in a word):

Supporting behavior(s):

WRAPPING UP

So, how did your day go? ☹ 😐 😀 🙂

What's your high-five to yourself?

Magical Moments:
(moments/people/experiences)

Intention you'd like to take into sleep with you?

Gratitude in Action

What separates privilege from entitlement is gratitude.
BRENÉ BROWN

Thank someone for something they don't know they offered you.

ACTION TAKEN:	FEELINGS EXPERIENCED:
THINGS LEARNED/ OBSERVED:	WOULD I DO THIS AGAIN? WHY?

If you don't take risks, you'll have a wasted soul.

DREW BARRYMORE

DATE _____ / _____ / 20_____

○ ○ ○ ○ ○ ○ ○
S M T W TH F S

GETTING STARTED

I am grateful for:

MARGIN
MADNESS

Today's intention (in a word):

Supporting behavior(s):

WRAPPING UP

So, how did your day go? ☹ 😐 🙂 😊

What's your high-five to yourself?

Magical Moments:
(moments/people/experiences)

Intention you'd like to take into sleep with you?

MUSINGS · POPPED UP · REMEMBER · THINK · DOODLE · INNOVATE

Amateurs sit and wait for inspiration, the rest of us just get up and go to work.

STEPHEN KING

DATE _____ / _____ / 20_____

○ ○ ○ ○ ○ ○ ○
S M T W TH F S

GETTING STARTED

I am grateful for:

Today's intention (in a word):

Supporting behavior(s):

MARGIN MADNESS

WRAPPING UP

So, how did your day go? ☹ 😐 😃 ☺

What's your high-five to yourself?

Magical Moments:
(moments/people/experiences)

Intention you'd like to take into sleep with you?

MUSINGS · POPPED UP · REMEMBER · THINK · DOODLE · INNOVATE

Put your ear down close to your soul and listen hard.
ANNE SEXTON

DATE ____ / ____ / 20____

○ ○ ○ ○ ○ ○ ○
S M T W TH F S

GETTING STARTED

I am grateful for:

MARGIN
MADNESS

Today's intention (in a word):

Supporting behavior(s):

WRAPPING UP

So, how did your day go? ☹ 😐 🙂 😊

What's your high-five to yourself?

Magical Moments:
(moments/people/experiences)

Intention you'd like to take into sleep with you?

MUSINGS · POPPED UP · REMEMBER · THINK · DOODLE · INNOVATE

I simply believe that some part of the human Self or Soul is not subject to the laws of space and time.

CARL JUNG

DATE _____ / _____ / 20_____

○ ○ ○ ○ ○ ○ ○
S M T W TH F S

GETTING STARTED

I am grateful for:

Today's intention (in a word):

MARGIN
MADNESS

Supporting behavior(s):

WRAPPING UP

So, how did your day go? ☹ 😐 🙂 😊

What's your high-five to yourself?

Magical Moments:
(moments/people/experiences)

Intention you'd like to take into sleep with you?

MUSINGS · POPPED UP · REMEMBER · THINK · DOODLE · INNOVATE

The best preparation for tomorrow is doing your best today.

H JACKSON BROWN, JR.

DATE ____ / ____ / 20____

○ ○ ○ ○ ○ ○ ○
S M T W TH F S

GETTING STARTED

I am grateful for:

MARGIN
MADNESS

Today's intention (in a word):

Supporting behavior(s):

INNOVATE · DOODLE · THINK · REMEMBER · POPPED UP · MUSINGS

WRAPPING UP

So, how did your day go? ☹ 😐 🙂 ☺

What's your high-five to yourself?

Magical Moments:
(moments/people/experiences)

Intention you'd like to take into sleep with you?

DATE ____ / ____ / 20____

○ ○ ○ ○ ○ ○ ○
S M T W TH F S

GETTING STARTED

I am grateful for:

Today's intention (in a word):

Supporting behavior(s):

MARGIN
MADNESS

WRAPPING UP

So, how did your day go? ☹ 😐 🙂 😊

What's your high-five to yourself?

Magical Moments:
(moments/people/experiences)

Intention you'd like to take into sleep with you?

MUSINGS · POPPED UP · REMEMBER · THINK · DOODLE · INNOVATE

Forgiveness is the fragrance the violet sheds on the heel that has crushed it.

MARK TWAIN

DATE ____ / ____ / 20____

O O O O O O O
S M T W TH F S

GETTING STARTED

I am grateful for:

MARGIN
MADNESS

Today's intention (in a word):

Supporting behavior(s):

WRAPPING UP

So, how did your day go? ☹ 😐 😊 🙂

What's your high-five to yourself?

Magical Moments:
(moments/people/experiences)

Intention you'd like to take into sleep with you?

MUSINGS · POPPED UP · REMEMBER · THINK · DOODLE · INNOVATE

Gratitude in Action

Ninety-nine percent of your thoughts are a complete waste of time. They do nothing but freak you out.

MICHAEL SINGER

Find someone you love/trust, and share a deep fear out loud.

ACTION TAKEN:	FEELINGS EXPERIENCED:
THINGS LEARNED/ OBSERVED:	WOULD I DO THIS AGAIN? WHY?

A leader will rise or fall within the culture they create.

ALEXSYS THOMPSON

DATE _____ / _____ / 20_____

○ ○ ○ ○ ○ ○ ○
S M T W TH F S

GETTING STARTED

I am grateful for:

MARGIN
MADNESS

Today's intention (in a word):

Supporting behavior(s):

WRAPPING UP

So, how did your day go? ☹ ☺ ☺ ☺

What's your high-five to yourself?

Magical Moments:
(moments/people/experiences)

Intention you'd like to take into sleep with you?

MUSINGS · POPPED UP · REMEMBER · THINK · DOODLE · INNOVATE

It's one of the greatest gifts you can give yourself, to forgive. Forgive everbody.

MAYA ANGELOU

DATE ____ / ____ / 20____

○ ○ ○ ○ ○ ○ ○
S M T W TH F S

GETTING STARTED

I am grateful for:

Today's intention (in a word):

Supporting behavior(s):

MARGIN
MADNESS

WRAPPING UP

So, how did your day go? ☹ 😐 😊 ☺

What's your high-five to yourself?

Magical Moments:
(moments/people/experiences)

Intention you'd like to take into sleep with you?

MUSINGS · POPPED UP · REMEMBER · THINK · DOODLE · INNOVATE

Dance is the hidden language of the soul of the body.
MARTHA GRAHAM

DATE ____ / ____ / 20____

○ ○ ○ ○ ○ ○ ○
S M T W TH F S

GETTING STARTED

I am grateful for:

MARGIN
MADNESS

Today's intention (in a word):

Supporting behavior(s):

WRAPPING UP

So, how did your day go? ☹ 😐 🙂 😊
What's your high-five to yourself?

Magical Moments:
(moments/people/experiences)

Intention you'd like to take into sleep with you?

INNOVATE · DOODLE · THINK · REMEMBER · POPPED UP · MUSINGS

The flower that follows the sun does so even on cloudy days.

ROBERT LEIGHTON

DATE ____ / ____ / 20____

O O O O O O O
S M T W TH F S

GETTING STARTED

I am grateful for:

Today's intention (in a word):

MARGIN
MADNESS

Supporting behavior(s):

WRAPPING UP

So, how did your day go? ☹ 😐 🙂 😊

What's your high-five to yourself?

Magical Moments:
(moments/people/experiences)

Intention you'd like to take into sleep with you?

MUSINGS · POPPED UP · REMEMBER · THINK · DOODLE · INNOVATE

You don't have to see the whole staircase, just take the first step.

MARTIN LUTHER KING, JR.

DATE ____ / ____ / 20____

○ ○ ○ ○ ○ ○ ○
S M T W TH F S

GETTING STARTED

I am grateful for:

MARGIN
MADNESS

Today's intention (in a word):

Supporting behavior(s):

MUSINGS · POPPED UP · REMEMBER · THINK · DOODLE · INNOVATE

WRAPPING UP

So, how did your day go? ☹ 😐 😊 ☺

What's your high-five to yourself?

Magical Moments:
(moments/people/experiences)

Intention you'd like to take into sleep with you?

On a deeper level you are already complete. When you realize that, there is a playful, joyous energy behind what you do.

ECKHART TOLLE

DATE ____ / ____ / 20____

○ ○ ○ ○ ○ ○ ○
S M T W TH F S

GETTING STARTED

I am grateful for:

Today's intention (in a word):

MARGIN
MADNESS

Supporting behavior(s):

WRAPPING UP

So, how did your day go? ☹ 😐 🙂 😊

What's your high-five to yourself?

Magical Moments:
(moments/people/experiences)

Intention you'd like to take into sleep with you?

MUSINGS · POPPED UP · REMEMBER · THINK · DOODLE · INNOVATE

Gratitude in Action

It doesn't interest me what you do for a living. I want to know what you ache for and if you dream of meeting your heart's longing.

ORIAH

Share your heart's deepest desire with a stranger. You can do this!

ACTION TAKEN:	FEELINGS EXPERIENCED:
THINGS LEARNED/ OBSERVED:	WOULD I DO THIS AGAIN? WHY?

Laughter is poison to fear.

GEORGE RR MARTIN

DATE ____ / ____ / 20____   ○ ○ ○ ○ ○ ○ ○
                                      S M T W TH F S

GETTING STARTED

I am grateful for:

Today's intention (in a word):

Supporting behavior(s):

MARGIN
MADNESS

WRAPPING UP

So, how did your day go? ☹ 😐 🙂 😊

What's your high-five to yourself?

Magical Moments:
(moments/people/experiences)

Intention you'd like to take into sleep with you?

MUSINGS · POPPED UP · REMEMBER · THINK · DOODLE · INNOVATE

You will never truly know yourself, or the strength of your relationships, until both have been tested by adversity.

JK ROWLING

DATE ____ / ____ / 20____

○ ○ ○ ○ ○ ○ ○
S M T W TH F S

GETTING STARTED

I am grateful for:

Today's intention (in a word):

Supporting behavior(s):

WRAPPING UP

So, how did your day go? ☹ 😐 😊 😄

What's your high-five to yourself?

Magical Moments:
(moments/people/experiences)

Intention you'd like to take into sleep with you?

Humility, that low, sweet root, from which all heavenly virtues shoot.

THOMAS MOORE

DATE _____ / _____ / 20_____

○ ○ ○ ○ ○ ○ ○
S M T W TH F S

GETTING STARTED

I am grateful for:

MARGIN
MADNESS

Today's intention (in a word):

Supporting behavior(s):

WRAPPING UP

So, how did your day go? ☹ 😕 🙂 😊

What's your high-five to yourself?

Magical Moments:
(moments/people/experiences)

Intention you'd like to take into sleep with you?

INNOVATE · DOODLE · THINK · REMEMBER · POPPED UP · MUSINGS

Love is taking a few steps backward maybe even more...
to give way to the happiness of the person you love.
WINNIE THE POOH

DATE ____ / ____ / 20____   ○ ○ ○ ○ ○ ○ ○
                                   S M T W TH F S

GETTING STARTED

I am grateful for:

Today's intention (in a word):

MARGIN
MADNESS

Supporting behavior(s):

WRAPPING UP

So, how did your day go? ☹ ☺ ☺ ☺

What's your high-five to yourself?

Magical Moments:
(moments/people/experiences)

Intention you'd like to take into sleep with you?

MUSINGS · POPPED UP · REMEMBER · THINK · DOODLE · INNOVATE

It is the soul's duty to be loyal to its own desires. It must abandon itself to its master passion.

DAME REBECCA WEST

DATE ____ / ____ / 20____   ○ ○ ○ ○ ○ ○ ○
                              S M T W TH F S

GETTING STARTED

I am grateful for:

Today's intention (in a word):

Supporting behavior(s):

MARGIN
MADNESS

WRAPPING UP

So, how did your day go? ☹ 😐 😊 😄

What's your high-five to yourself?

Magical Moments:
(moments/people/experiences)

Intention you'd like to take into sleep with you?

MUSINGS · POPPED UP · REMEMBER · THINK · DOODLE · INNOVATE

What you think, you become. What you feel, you attract,
What you imagine, you create.

BUDDHA

DATE ____ / ____ / 20____   O O O O O O O
                              S M T W TH F S

GETTING STARTED

I am grateful for:

MARGIN
MADNESS

Today's intention (in a word):

Supporting behavior(s):

INNOVATE · DOODLE · THINK · REMEMBER · POPPED UP · MUSINGS

WRAPPING UP

So, how did your day go? ☹ 😐 🙂 😊

What's your high-five to yourself?

Magical Moments:
(moments/people/experiences)

Intention you'd like to take into sleep with you?

Sometimes even to live is and act of courage.

SENECA

DATE ____ / ____ / 20____

○ ○ ○ ○ ○ ○ ○
S M T W TH F S

GETTING STARTED

I am grateful for:

Today's intention (in a word):

Supporting behavior(s):

MARGIN
MADNESS

WRAPPING UP

So, how did your day go? ☹ 🙁 🙂 😊

What's your high-five to yourself?

Magical Moments:
(moments/people/experiences)

Intention you'd like to take into sleep with you?

MUSINGS · POPPED UP · REMEMBER · THINK · DOODLE · INNOVATE

To dare is to lose one's footing momentarily. To not dare is to lose oneself.

SOREN KIERKEGAARD

DATE ____ / ____ / 20____

○ ○ ○ ○ ○ ○ ○
S M T W TH F S

GETTING STARTED

I am grateful for:

MARGIN
MADNESS

Today's intention (in a word):

Supporting behavior(s):

WRAPPING UP

So, how did your day go? ☹ 😐 😊 😃

What's your high-five to yourself?

Magical Moments:
(moments/people/experiences)

Intention you'd like to take into sleep with you?

INNOVATE · DOODLE · THINK · REMEMBER · POPPED UP · MUSINGS

Gratitude in Action

One looks back with appreciation to the brilliant teachers, but with gratitude to those who touched our human feelings.

CARL JUNG

Reach out to a mentor/teacher, and express the value they have added to your life.

ACTION TAKEN:	FEELINGS EXPERIENCED:
THINGS LEARNED/ OBSERVED:	**WOULD I DO THIS AGAIN? WHY?**

Words are a pretext. It is the inner bond that draws one person to another, not words.

RUMI

DATE _____ / _____ / 20_____

○ ○ ○ ○ ○ ○ ○
S M T W TH F S

GETTING STARTED

I am grateful for:

MARGIN
MADNESS

Today's intention (in a word):

Supporting behavior(s):

WRAPPING UP

So, how did your day go? ☹ 😐 🙂 😊

What's your high-five to yourself?

Magical Moments:
(moments/people/experiences)

Intention you'd like to take into sleep with you?

INNOVATE · DOODLE · THINK · REMEMBER · POPPED UP · MUSINGS

That man is richest whose pleasures are cheapest.

HENRY DAVID THOREAU

DATE ____ / ____ / 20____

○ ○ ○ ○ ○ ○ ○
S M T W TH F S

GETTING STARTED

I am grateful for:

Today's intention (in a word):

MARGIN
MADNESS

Supporting behavior(s):

WRAPPING UP

So, how did your day go? ☹ 😐 🙂 😊

What's your high-five to yourself?

Magical Moments:
(moments/people/experiences)

Intention you'd like to take into sleep with you?

MUSINGS · POPPED UP · REMEMBER · THINK · DOODLE · INNOVATE

Optimism is a happiness magnet. If you stay positive, good things and good people will be drawn to you.

MARY LOU RETTON

DATE _____ / _____ / 20_____

○ ○ ○ ○ ○ ○ ○
S M T W TH F S

GETTING STARTED

I am grateful for:

MARGIN
MADNESS

Today's intention (in a word):

Supporting behavior(s):

WRAPPING UP

So, how did your day go? ☹ 😐 🙂 😊

What's your high-five to yourself?

Magical Moments:
(moments/people/experiences)

Intention you'd like to take into sleep with you?

MUSINGS · POPPED UP · REMEMBER · THINK · DOODLE · INNOVATE

Being happy doesn't mean everything is perfect. It means you've decided to look beyond the imperfection.

AUTHOR UNKNOWN

DATE ____ / ____ / 20____   O O O O O O O
                                    S M T W TH F S

GETTING STARTED

I am grateful for:

Today's intention (in a word):

MARGIN
MADNESS

Supporting behavior(s):

WRAPPING UP

So, how did your day go? ☹ 😐 🙂 😊

What's your high-five to yourself?

Magical Moments:
(moments/people/experiences)

Intention you'd like to take into sleep with you?

MUSINGS · POPPED UP · REMEMBER · THINK · DOODLE · INNOVATE

No act of kindness, no matter how small, is ever wasted.

AESOP

DATE _____ / _____ / 20_____

○ ○ ○ ○ ○ ○ ○
S M T W TH F S

GETTING STARTED

I am grateful for:

MARGIN
MADNESS

Today's intention (in a word):

Supporting behavior(s):

WRAPPING UP

So, how did your day go? 😣 😐 😊 ☺

What's your high-five to yourself?

Magical Moments:
(moments/people/experiences)

Intention you'd like to take into sleep with you?

MUSINGS · POPPED UP · REMEMBER · THINK · DOODLE · INNOVATE

I'd far rather be happy than right any day.

DOUGLAS ADAMS

DATE _____ / _____ / 20_____

○ ○ ○ ○ ○ ○ ○
S M T W TH F S

GETTING STARTED

I am grateful for:

Today's intention (in a word):

MARGIN
MADNESS

Supporting behavior(s):

WRAPPING UP

So, how did your day go? ☹ 😐 🙂 😊

What's your high-five to yourself?

Magical Moments:
(moments/people/experiences)

Intention you'd like to take into sleep with you?

MUSINGS · POPPED UP · REMEMBER · THINK · DOODLE · INNOVATE

Diversity is the one true thing we all have in common.
Celebrate it every day.
AUTHOR UNKNOWN

DATE ____ / ____ / 20____   ○ ○ ○ ○ ○ ○ ○
                             S M T W TH F S

GETTING STARTED

I am grateful for:

MARGIN
MADNESS

Today's intention (in a word):

Supporting behavior(s):

WRAPPING UP

So, how did your day go? ☹ 😐 🙂 😊

What's your high-five to yourself?

Magical Moments:
(moments/people/experiences)

Intention you'd like to take into sleep with you?

MUSINGS · POPPED UP · REMEMBER · THINK · DOODLE · INNOVATE

Your own soul is nourished when you are kind; it is destroyed when you are cruel.

KING SOLOMON

DATE ____ / ____ / 20____

○ ○ ○ ○ ○ ○ ○
S M T W TH F S

GETTING STARTED

I am grateful for:

Today's intention (in a word):

MARGIN
MADNESS

Supporting behavior(s):

WRAPPING UP

So, how did your day go? ☹ 😐 🙂 😊

What's your high-five to yourself?

Magical Moments:
(moments/people/experiences)

Intention you'd like to take into sleep with you?

MUSINGS · POPPED UP · REMEMBER · THINK · DOODLE · INNOVATE

And remember, no matter where you go, there you are.

CONFUCIUS

DATE ____ / ____ / 20____

○ ○ ○ ○ ○ ○ ○
S M T W TH F S

GETTING STARTED

I am grateful for:

MARGIN
MADNESS

Today's intention (in a word):

Supporting behavior(s):

WRAPPING UP

So, how did your day go? ☹ 😐 🙂 😊

What's your high-five to yourself?

Magical Moments:
(moments/people/experiences)

Intention you'd like to take into sleep with you?

MUSINGS · POPPED UP · REMEMBER · THINK · DOODLE · INNOVATE

CONGRATS
YOU DID IT!

Congratulations!

Thank you for your time and commitment to your gratitude journey. You have changed the world far beyond what you have personally experienced. Through this process, your ability to suspend judgment and be curious has created space for people to show up differently with you. That shifts their experience of being the best version of themselves.

When we find the grace and beauty of the world around us in the small things and tough times, we increase our ability to be more accountable for our own destiny. This frees us up to explore spaces within and expand our awareness of the awesomeness we have within each of us.

I hope you find yourself feeling proud and not wanting to stop your gratitude practice.

If that is the case, I am happy to extend a discount for the second journey in this series. Together, they are designed to cover 365 entries. Please visit my webpage at www.alexsysthompson.com/gratitudejournal and enter your email. We will send you a coupon code to use in purchasing your next journal.

Send a video of your experience to grateful@ alexsysthompson.com, and the first 96 people will receive a second journal, free. We will also have other gratitude products, groups, and conversations for you to take part in as one of the first 96 to pioneer the journey. Please note, it's the first 96 to send in a video, not purchase a journal.

I would also love to hear your experience of this journey. Feel free to drop me an email, or visit my Facebook page and share. Here's to you and the rest of your amazing life full of gratitude.

In deep gratitude,

Alexsys

MY EXPERIENCE

Use this page to write whatever feels right about your journey through these pages.